Every Day Is a Gift

A Couple's Cancer Journey

—∞—

Margaret P. and **John F. McEwan**

"In *Every Day Is a Gift,* Margaret McEwan tells the story of her husband's life following the diagnosis of metastatic melanoma, and how together they navigated the ups and downs of treatment and clinical trials. Margaret captures the essence of living well with cancer and how compassionate care and upfront communication by the medical team impacts not only the care of the patient but also the bereavement experience for the family. A must read for families and clinicians." —**Sue Morris, PsyD.**, Director of Bereavement Services, Dana-Farber Cancer Institute, Boston.

Every Day Is a Gift, *A Couple's Cancer Journey,* Published May, 2018
Cover Design: Howard Johnson
Interior Design and Layout: Howard Johnson
Editorial and proofreading services: Eden Rivers Editorial Services;
Karen Grennan
Photo Credits:
Aimedon, *Northern Cardinal Male.* Dreamstime.
Bruyeu, Ryhor, *Sunshine Sunset Sunrise In Beautiful Birch Forest In Summer Season.*
Dreamstime.
Author photo courtesy of Julie McEwan Swan.

 **SDP Publishing**

Published by SDP Publishing, an imprint of SDP Publishing Solutions, LLC.

To obtain permission(s) to use material from this work, please submit a written
request to:
SDP Publishing
Permissions Department
PO Box 26, East Bridgewater, MA 02333
or email your request to info@SDPPublishing.com.

ISBN-13 (print): 978-0-9992839-8-1
ISBN-13 (e-book): 978-0-9992839-9-8
Library of Congress Control Number: 2018936902

Printed in the United States of America

To John, who taught us all how to laugh, love, and live life to the fullest.

To our family, friends, and the caregivers who supported us throughout our cancer journey.

To those who follow in our footsteps, may you find the face of hope and purpose every day of your journey.

It Takes a Village of Caretakers, Family, Friends, and Hope

This book is a memoir about a family living with a cancer diagnosis and the places where we found hope. The purpose of telling our story is to share how hope may be found in unlikely places and through people you encounter—sometimes even strangers. Cancer gives a whole new meaning to life and changes your perspective on what's important—every day!

The story chronicles the journey that my husband, John, and I shared over the last five years of his life. Like every couple, we had our share of joys and struggles, but we were happily married for more than 40 years. However happy we thought we were before he was diagnosed with Stage IV melanoma, we became even closer—and life together became even more precious—as we shared his cancer diagnosis and treatments. Even though John was not retired, we both knew that these years of living with cancer, however many they may be, would be our retirement years together.

John always had lived every aspect of life fully and chose to face his cancer diagnosis head-on. Because of this, he did not want the disease to define him. He wanted to use it as one more opportunity to defy the odds, and in the process continue to live with joy and purpose to the very end. He died at peace with himself and everyone he knew, a very happy and fulfilled man. He is remembered for his infectious laugh, great sense of humor, and love for his family, his friends, and the students and staff he encountered throughout his educational career. The thing he valued most in his life were his relationships with people.

My hope is that our story will bring someone else comfort and hope as they live their cancer journey with a loved one. It takes effort to see the brighter side of a challenging situation, but our motto throughout our 40-year marriage was: "Every day is a gift." May you live your life fully appreciating that every day can be special. Our commitment to ourselves must be to wake up every day and find out how.

M. McEwan

Preface

Yesterday is history, tomorrow is a mystery,
today is a gift of God, which is why
we call it the present.
— **Bill Keane**

To capture the ups and downs of our cancer journey, I thought it best to chronicle our journey as it happened. This book is made up of a series of my letters and e-mails and John's unedited letters and e-mails to his staff. The narrative provides you, the reader, additional background information about our story not revealed in the letters and e-mails.

To help me focus during the doctor's office visits, I always had a notebook with me. I would write down what was being said. This helped me to listen and to ask questions as treatments and prescriptions were changed to accommodate the side effects of the cancer treatments. There were extreme highs and lows every time we had to change course. John used to say to our oncologist that as long as he had options to offer us, he was optimistic that he would find the right "cocktail" to stem the growth of his unique cancer.

There were so many people who were supporting us on this journey that I used my notes to create updates on John's progress through e-mails. During the ride home from the hospital John would ask me, "How can we market the message we've been given?" We would agree on what we would tell our family and friends about the visit. Every time he had results from a scan or a change of treatment plan, I would send out an update. I found this to be a cathartic exercise for me. Moreover, it was too emotionally draining to repeat the story verbally again and again. The responses that we received from these e-mails became our biggest source of support and love throughout our cancer journey. It gave so many people, including John's former students and colleagues, a chance to connect with us, many who may not have taken the time under different circumstances.

The e-mails eventually circulated far beyond my original list of recipients. (A former student actually reprinted them on a Facebook page called the "John McEwan Great Teacher Tribute Page.") John was a public figure in the community. With that in mind, I was very careful not to reveal too much detail of what was actually happening in real time other than to our own children and immediate family. After John's death, many people suggested that I reprint the e-mails to offer hope to others.

During the five years that John lived with cancer, he agreed that he would do whatever it would take to survive. However, he wanted quality time not just quantity. And quality time he got, but not without some very frightening periods. When he first told his staff of his illness, he described the cancer journey as a scary, dark amusement park ride with many twists and turns and ups and downs.

When John asked our oncologist directly about his prognosis the doctor was reluctant to give him a timeline. John wanted to know because he was a planner. He wanted to make the most of whatever time the doctors thought he might have. The doctor reluctantly answered that at his advanced stage of melanoma, the average rate of survival at the time was probably six months to a year. John took that as a challenge that he would exceed the averages and he did. He truly lived, worked, and loved life fully for five years after his diagnosis.

At that time, we made a conscious decision not to share the prognosis for life expectancy even with our children. Of course they could research this for themselves, but we were determined we would defy the odds and not share the original timeline until after we had surpassed it.

With John's spirit and optimism you might expect that life had been always good for him. Surprisingly, he came from a highly dysfunctional family. The only stability in his life was his formal education. He never regretted any part of his life experiences because he felt that they helped to shape the person that he became. Because he had survived some pretty tough times in his early life, he always tried very hard, but was never confident that he had achieved the high standards he had set for himself as a teacher, an administrator, or a role model.

When a challenge presented itself, he would evaluate the situation, determine what needed to be done, and then set goals to accomplish what he wanted. As an educator, John always felt a responsibility in both his thoughts and actions to be a positive role model in how he approached life. He was not going to allow a cancer diagnosis to define him as a person.

From the time John became a school administrator, he communicated through letters to his staff, especially at Thanksgiving and Christmas. It was a reflection of how he felt the year was going and a message of hope that no matter what problems the school or schools faced during that particular year, there was always something to celebrate. This first letter was written five months before John was diagnosed.

—ᴍ—

Holiday Letter to Whitman-Hanson Staff, December 2007

The best advice I could give any of you at this holiday season is to take time to enjoy each other and to reconnect. In reconnecting with the ones you love, I really believe that you reconnect with yourself. The holiday season is an opportunity to really sit down and discuss what is really important—not what you are giving or getting regarding gifts—but who is important in your life and then telling them why they are important. Some of the most treasured gifts I have given or received are a note, a card, a letter, or even a notebook of shared thoughts about a loved one. It takes some reflection and honesty but it is truly worth it.

The holidays, more than any other time of the year, are an occasion for hope. I believe it is why a baby (not just Santa) is the real symbol of the season for most of us. Hope is not always fashionable in our fast-paced world. Hope implies understanding, patience, and forgiveness. These are tough virtues to embrace sometimes, but they can help us to refocus and to remain positive no matter what obstacles we face. It's because we are hopeful that we make New Year's resolutions every year in spite of past disappointments. We always should strive to get better every year in every way possible!

Over the past few years, the greatest sense of hope for me has been the birth of our two grandchildren: Zachary and Keira. I swore I

would not be another obnoxious grandparent
but, if you aren't a grandparent yet, just wait
... it's impossible to pull it off! It's all because of
hope. In the eyes of your grandchild or, really, in
the eyes of any child that we interact with every
day in our schools, we see hope for the future,
innocence, and unending dreams. Although we
have to admit that we have had to grow up, we can
wish, like Peter Pan, that we still had a simpler,
happier life....

    John

1

The Beginning of the Journey

*Things don't happen for a reason, you have to
find a purpose for why things happen.*
—John McEwan

"You have cancer." When these three words are
spoken, your life as you know it immediately
changes! The world starts to close in and you
narrow your focus. You are entering a world of unknowns.

We always said that "we" had cancer because we were
both living with it. As a married couple, our cancer journey
was a shared experience. My husband, John, received the
shattering news—eight weeks after in situ surgery to
remove a malignant tumor on his scalp—that his cancer
had metastasized into stage IV melanoma. Even though
one person is given the cancer diagnosis the caregiver also
lives with the fear, the despair, and the hope and belief that
if you have the best available medical care, you choose the
right attitude, and you have faith that God will guide you
in your path, together you can overcome the odds.

Every marriage that lasts more than forty years has high points and low points. If you are blessed with a good marriage, the love you had in the beginning of your relationship continues to grow and mature with time, and carries you through the journey. Living with a terminal illness has its challenges. It also allows you to reflect on what is important in your life and what is not. We called this one of the gifts of cancer. During the last five years of our marriage, we lived fully every single day because we knew each day that we had together was a blessing.

John was still working full-time as a school superintendent. I was retired and he had planned to retire the next year. We had celebrated 36 happy years together. With three adult children, two of whom were married, and two grandchildren, our lives were joy-filled and blessed. Time spent with our family and making memories with them was very important to us. We enjoyed traveling together, and with the whole family, as often as we could.

From the start of our married life, we knew we were fortunate and never took a day for granted. We found something to celebrate each day. The recurring theme of our life together had been and continued to be: "Every day is a gift." Certainly, some gifts were better than others, but all were to be treasured because each day was precious.

John was an eternal optimist, but always a realist. He truly felt that things happened for a purpose and that we had to make sense of our lives by how we embraced life's challenges. He would find a new purpose in his life by being given a terminal cancer diagnosis. He wanted to show others that life was worth living even if you were living under a cloud.

The circle of our cancer life began with the addition of a new family member. The day that our third grandchild was born was the day we learned that John's cancer had metastasized.

CHAPTER

2

The Initial Diagnosis and Treatment

We are lucky where we live and when we live.
—John McEwan

In the spring of 2008, John had decided to retire from his position as Superintendent of Schools of the Whitman-Hanson Regional School District. At the time he made the decision he did not know that he had cancer.

In late January, we noticed a white growth on his scalp that appeared to be a fatty tumor. I asked him to get it checked. He had a body scan by his primary care physician, but forgot to mention the fatty tumor on his scalp and the doctor did not see it. About a month later, we were vacationing in Hawaii when we noticed it was bleeding. On May 8, 2008, John went to a local dermatologist to have it evaluated. The doctor took a biopsy and said he would be in touch. This initial procedure was done in the office, but it was very painful. Later, John would say that is was one of the most painful procedures he had to endure throughout the course of his many treatments.

Several days after the office visit, we were hosting a rather noisy family get-together when the home phone rang. Whoever happened to answer it said it was for John. I heard him say: "Oh, yes, I have been waiting for your call," and he immediately left the room. A few minutes later he came back to get a pen and paper and again left the room. John often received phone calls related to work in the evening, but I could tell by his inaudible responses and his tone that this was no ordinary phone call. He returned to the room, hung up the phone, and sat down in his chair looking ashen and solemn. The chatter in the room continued around him, but he was clearly preoccupied by this phone call. I asked quietly if everything was all right. He said, "I'll tell you later."

John did not move from his chair for the remainder of the visit. He made attempts to stay engaged in the moment but I knew he was distracted. After our guests left I knelt down beside him and asked, "So what was the phone call about?" Shaking his head in disbelief in a quivering voice he said, "It was the dermatologist. He said the biopsy test results have come back. He said, 'You have metastatic melanoma and you will be dead within five years.' He wanted me to write down the name and phone number of a head and neck surgeon from Tufts Medical Center that he recommended who could remove the malignant tumor from my head."

I was outraged that he would receive this kind of news with a phone call. I said, "I do not believe this. We are going somewhere else for a second opinion." This was our introduction to the world of cancer treatment. Fortunately for us, it was one of the few times that we were treated without compassion.

John called the surgeon's office that he was referred to the next day and was told he needed to make several appointments for lab work, a pre-op appointment, an

MRI, and CT scans. He needed to be seen the day before surgery to inject dyes and radioactive substances that would assist the surgeon in identifying the lymph nodes that may contain cancer cells. This procedure is called mapping. All of these procedures required strict instructions on whether or not you must fast and what medications you may have to stop taking temporarily. This first phone call in itself was stressful.

Perhaps not by coincidence, on our way into the hospital to meet with the surgeon for the first time, we met a woman from our hometown coming out of the hospital's main entrance. She had just left her oncologist's office. She was elated because she had been given the news that her cancer was stable. This was such a positive message to receive as we began our cancer journey.

The best thing the local dermatologist did for us was to refer John to this otolaryngologist at Tufts Medical Center in Boston. Although surgeons are not typically noted for their bedside manner, we found this surgeon and everyone in his office to be respectful, compassionate, and competent in their treatment of both of us. We were in good hands.

In filling out the paperwork for this visit, naturally we were asked for our insurance numbers, etc. Ironically, in the fall of 2007 John was offered cancer insurance as part of his compensation package. At the time, he told the school's business manager that no one in his family had ever had cancer, but he might as well sign up for it since it was being offered.

Health insurance generally covers all of the tests, procedures, medications, and hospitalizations. It does not cover expenses related to accessing services such as getting to and from appointments, parking, accommodations (if necessary), or meals. Cancer insurance helps to defray incidental costs not covered by health insurance.

The surgeon's office manager told us, "I recommend

that everyone in this office sign up for it." She explained the lifetime risk of developing cancer for men is one in two and for women is one in three. It does not mean that cancer will be the cause of death but the risks are high that it will occur. As the reality of paying for incidental expenses hit us, we felt fortunate to have this extra coverage.

After reading the scan results, the surgeon recommended that John have the lesion removed as well as the satellite tissue and lymph nodes near the site. We were told that the surgery would leave a deep depression in John's scalp that could later be considered for plastic surgery. The surgery that took place on an outpatient basis on June 26, 2008 was deemed a success. There was no sign of cancer in the satellite tissue or the lymph nodes. We dedicated that summer to John's physical healing and emotional support.

We would later refer to that summer as our honeymoon from cancer.

The surgeon had forewarned us that there was a fifty-fifty chance that the melanoma had already spread somewhere else in the body. We naively believed that the surgery was going to be the "cure" for John's cancer.

The Tufts' surgeon referred us to a medical oncologist at Massachusetts General Hospital for follow up. Little did we know at our first meeting with Dr. Donald Lawrence in July of 2008 where our cancer journey would take us. We could not have been assigned to a more competent physician in the field of melanoma nor a more compassionate person; what a stroke of luck as we started our path on this journey with cancer.

Before anyone is seen at Mass General, a seven-digit patient identification number is assigned. This number is used every time there is interaction with anyone or any service. Both John and I expected that because Mass General is such a big hospital, the personnel and the service would be very impersonal, just like the number. Much to our surprise, we never ever felt reduced to that number. It served as a tool to ensure accuracy of identification, but the patient's name was always used when interacting with the staff.

As you turn the corner from the elevators to enter Mass General Hospital's outpatient infusion center, the view takes your breath away. The center is located on the eighth floor of the Yawkey Building on the main campus. The hallway is a wall of glass windows with sunlit panoramic views of Boston's Back Bay area. The design of the building and the view had an amazingly calming effect on us from the first day we visited the center. It reminded us that although we were coming to grips with a powerful personal health issue, we were still part of the outside world, if we chose to take in the view.

The first person we met in the infusion center was a receptionist named Mohammedi. She was very pleasant yet professional. She patiently explained what the procedures were for checking in and what to expect during our visits. The time she took to explain what we should anticipate during that first visit helped to alleviate our anxiety. As we got to know her better in our follow-up visits she would always perform her check-in duties and then ask, "So how are the grandchildren doing? What are they up to?"

As every cancer patient knows, even though there is a daily schedule, the time spent waiting for an infusion chair or bed can add unexpected delays to your visit. John became such a familiar face in the infusion center that every one of the receptionists at the check-in desk would make every attempt to assign him to the same private room. They would tease him by saying, "The McEwan Suite is waiting for you!"

This group was and is representative of what contributes to the "Everyday Amazing" experience at Mass General's Cancer Center. People who work in and around cancer centers have a special calling and those who are afflicted with this disease are very fortunate that there are people who dedicate themselves to this specialized field of medical care. Although the conditions were not what we would have chosen, the days we spent in the infusion center would prove to be some of the most valued time we would share as a married couple. By example, John was teaching and reinforcing the message that we must learn to live fully in the moment.

Dr. Lawrence was respectful of John, and me, and treated John as a whole person. John was not just a patient with cancer, but a person with legitimate emotions related to living life as fully as possible. At our first meeting with Dr. Lawrence he asked John, "How are you handling the diagnosis?" John said, "Of course I did not want to believe it, but I certainly have had enough happen in my life that would not leave me questioning: *Why me?* Why not me? I am just as vulnerable as the next person to get this disease. I am a person of faith and I think God is testing me."

John promised Dr. Lawrence that he would be his best patient. He explained that the day he had his first visit with the local dermatologist on May 8, he had been offered the position of president of the high school where he had graduated from 43 years before. In the meantime, he had one year left in his contract before he officially retired as superintendent of the Whitman-Hanson Regional School District. Together, with the family, he had places he wanted to go and things to see and he did not want cancer to stand in his way.

John always said: "We are lucky where we live and when we live." We felt so incredibly fortunate to have such world-class medical facilities close to home and to be where the latest advances in medical treatment could be offered.

We were advised that when a patient has undergone surgery, it is good medical practice to allow the body to heal and to not subject it to additional treatments for six to eight weeks. We had planned a brief trip to Disney World over Labor Day weekend with our daughters and grandchildren. This trip became symbolic to John that he was going to live life to the fullest as long as he could.

The scheduled return date from our trip would mark the start of the ninth week after John's surgery. Dr. Lawrence explained that John's case of melanoma appeared to be slow growing, but nevertheless, melanoma is an aggressive, out-of-control type of cancer. We had to promise to start Interferon treatments as soon as we got back.

Interferon is a class of proteins known as cytokines that our bodies make in response to viral, bacterial, parasitic infections, and tumor cells. When the synthetic version is given in high doses it makes patients feel like they have flu-like symptoms: body aches, fatigue, fevers, itchy rashes, and appetite loss. It is designed to boost the immune system and to slow the cancer growth. The treatment is a commitment of five days a week for four weeks on an outpatient basis. The intravenous treatments last about two hours a day. We were told that an IV would be inserted each day for the treatment. Dr. Lawrence did not usually use chemo ports for his melanoma patients because of the potential risk for infection. This concerned John because medical personnel had always had trouble accessing his veins, and we had to wait and see how things would proceed.

If the patient completes the initial four weeks of treatment, a maintenance phase is established that consists of subcutaneous injections three times a week for 48 weeks— or for as long as the drug is tolerated—and as long as no new cancer sites are found. Dr. Lawrence explained the risks associated with taking the drug. He also told us that large studies had recently reported successful treatment had shown the average patient follow-up had gone from seven years to twelve to fifteen years. This was encouraging news to us.

CHAPTER

3

Treatment Options:
the Highs and Lows

God grant me the serenity to accept the things
I cannot change; courage to change the things
I can; and wisdom to know the difference.
—Reinhold Niebuhr

During our hospital visit on the ninth day of Interferon treatments, John complained to me about severe pain in his leg near the skin graft that was taken to repair the site of the tumor removed from his head. I told him he should mention it to the nurse practitioner on our oncology team. She recommended that John go for scans that day to determine if there was a medical reason for the pain or if it was heightened nerve sensitivity in the area of the skin graft.

The order to have new scans was a simple recommendation. The difficult part was finding a location to get the PET scan and MRIs scheduled that day. There was no time available for scans or an MRI at the main hospital so we were forced to take a shuttle bus from the main campus of

Massachusetts General to an offsite location in Chelsea, four and a half miles away. The distance was not long, but when a patient is in pain physically and emotionally, the trip in city traffic is overwhelming. The whole process from the time the order was given to the time we returned to the hospital took over five hours. And then we had to wait when we got back for a consultation with our oncologist. We always appreciated the fact that the hospital staff took into consideration that we wanted to minimize the number of trips into and out of the city. But this often meant we had very long days there.

When the new MRI and PET scans were made available to our oncologist he reported to us that John's cancer had already metastasized. The honeymoon period of dealing with cancer was over.

Up until that point, there had been no evidence of sites anywhere but the initial lesion on John's head. With the new scans, it was determined that there were three sites that would be tagged—or measured for growth—going forward. Dr. Lawrence discussed the first few options available to us for treatment. He strongly recommended that John be given an immediate two-week course of radiation as an outpatient. The radiation would not eliminate the cancer, but it would stabilize John for the next treatment.

We met with the radiation oncologist who was very reassuring that radiation treatments of a two-week duration did not generally cause side effects. She said that the most difficult part would most likely be the commute to get in and out of Boston for a ten to fifteen-minute appointment. We live only 24 miles from the hospital, but it takes between one and a half to two hours to commute one way.

On the way home from the first radiation treatment, I remember having to pull over because John had gotten sick to his stomach. Because cancer patients are so vulnerable, you are advised to call the doctor for any changes in symptoms at all. Since the nausea was not anticipated, I called the hospital to check on what I should do to treat him. Fortunately, Dr. Lawrence was on call and telephoned us right back. He reassured us that, "Although nausea is not a typical side effect from radiation, you should not worry because John had just undergone the Interferon treatments." He recommended, "Just proceed as you normally would to treat nausea." Other than fatigue, this was the only adverse reaction John had to radiation.

After the radiation treatments were completed, we were offered two choices. The first was a clinical trial that Dr. Lawrence thought might stunt the growth of the lesions. The second option was Interleukin-2 that is a very aggressive treatment requiring hospitalization. "Interleukin-2," Dr. Lawrence explained, "is always available to you as an option, but the slots in clinical trials are only available periodically and John would have to qualify for a slot."

It was during this first series of counseling sessions that we knew we were dealing with the right doctor for us. Dr. Lawrence encouraged us to look into any clinical trial that was offered anywhere in the world and if we wanted to pursue it, even if it meant we must leave Mass General, he would do what he could to help us. By offering this option to us we knew that he was putting us in charge of John's care, and that he would not stand in our way if we felt there was something available to us that he or Mass General could not provide.

We opted for the clinical trial that required going to the hospital weekly for an intravenous injection. The length of the trial was three months. After that time, scans would be done, and we would be given an update on the status of the cancer cells. The best part of this clinical trial was that it allowed John to return to work. He felt more fatigued than usual, but he did not have flu-like symptoms. It gave us three months of "normalcy" that brought us through the Christmas holidays.

———— ∿ ————

Letter to Faculty and Staff
October 3, 2008

Dear Members of the Whitman-Hanson Community:

Normally, I wait until just before Thanksgiving or the Christmas season before I send you a letter like this one. There is a great deal I would like to share with you. I have learned over the past few months that there are things you can plan for and control ... and things you just have to accept. It's my nature to want to choose my direction and then to do my best to move personally and professionally in that direction ... however, I have learned that we all have some limits.

I know some of you might be thinking, "Here comes McEwan's Last Lecture" or, if it's Tuesday, this must be about Morrie. Although I am the first to admit that I am a sentimentalist, this e-mail is not about those thoughts. It's about what I have learned over the past few months that I would like to share with all of you.

First of all, I am so happy to announce that on September 15, my son, Chris, and his wife, Liz, had their first child ... and my third grandchild. The baby was huge (9 lbs. 5 oz.) and they called him Maxwell. Maxwell ... they wanted a Scottish name. On the day the baby was born we finally asked about the Maxwell's middle name; you can imagine how Margaret and I filled up

when they told us it was "John." What a shocker!!!!
I could not have been happier or prouder! We will
go down to see the "new" family in Charlotte later
this month, if health issues continue to be in
abeyance. Chris also called us last night to let us
know that he had just been made a vice president
in his company. What a great time for them!

My family, as a whole, has been terrific, as
we have taken this journey in the dark, like so
many rides in Disney World. You don't know
where you are going but the exhilaration of the
trip is a "high." I did get down to Orlando Labor
Day weekend and spent a few unforgettable
days with my wife, daughters, son-in-law and
grandchildren. It was a special time and I spent
the second half of the trip planning my next
vacation. You have got to have something to look
forward to! I have learned that "no regrets" needs
to be part of our daily vocabulary!

When I announced my intent to retire
last spring, I had no idea about the cancer. I
also had no idea that Cardinal Spellman, my
high school alma mater, would be offering me a
post-retirement position that would be difficult
to refuse. It would not be the same as working
at Whitman-Hanson, but the pace would be
different, and it would be like going "full-circle"
in my career. It seemed like the natural thing to
do and, now, it just seems so much like a part of
that dark ride at Disney with its many twists
and turns. I do believe things happen for a purpose
and that we make sense of our lives by how we
embrace life's challenges.

My wife has been amazing over the past few
weeks. In fact, she has put off her own required hip

surgery until we have a clearer picture of what's around the bend for the two of us. I must admit that I have had some fairly scary, lonely, and painful days over the past few months but, I also must admit, that most of them have been positive and the opportunity to be reflective has been a real blessing. I am so thankful that Margaret and I and so many of our friends and relatives have shared memories and dreams and have had many rowdy laughs and some quiet, emotional hugs.

I am especially thankful that our schools continue to move in the right direction. The school committee has been amazing by allowing me to work from my home. The peace of mind it has afforded me and the way it has kept me very busy in a positive direction has been a great gift. Special thanks to Ruth, Sharon, Craig, Milly, Michelle and the others in central office. In each school, from the principals to each individual who may work only two hours a day, I appreciate the sense of normalcy, productivity, and positive energy I get from my communications with individuals in each of the buildings. The people in Whitman and Hanson are very, very fortunate to have such dedicated educators and support staff!

When I was first diagnosed with cancer last May, I misunderstood the doctor and I heard that with surgery things would be all clear and, except for that hole in my head, life would continue as usual. In the summer, I was referred to a great cancer specialist at Mass General. His diagnosis still was optimistic … it just was not open-ended.

The doctor from MGH recommended a "chemo" therapy known as Interferon. There would be side effects and it was not a cure, but it would help fight off any future infection. I was "gung-ho," but my body rejected the Interferon. Today I finish my therapy for radiation and yesterday I completed my biopsy. (They think there is cancer in my lung and ribs but they won't know for sure until next week.)

I have been out of my office for a long time, but you must know that I have not been away from work ... even for one day. I plan to "be the best patient" any of my doctors have ever had. (You don't want to mess up this kind of relationship, especially if you don't know what's around the next corner!) My goal, although it's been my goal for the past three weeks, is to come back into the office part time starting next week. I will continue to get direction from the doctors and I know I will continue to get positive energy from all of you.

Thanks again for your prayers ... your notes and cards ... your e-mails ... and your commitment to your kids. Everything is greatly appreciated! I will keep you updated on my next steps, but you can be sure that I will have no surprises for you ... just a positive attitude. I can STILL choose my attitude!

I wish you all the best throughout the rest of the 2008-2009 school year. Please do not hesitate to contact me if you need anything at all! As Browning said, "The best is yet to come!"

Sincerely,
John

———

Every time John went to the hospital for treatments, he had to have blood drawn for laboratory tests and intravenous lines inserted for IV fluids and medication. On one day, three different experienced nurses, one a special IV nurse, were called in and tried 13 different times over the course of eight hours to access his veins. They met with some success, but John's veins were particularly small and at times would collapse after a short period of time. It was painful for him. An implanted port-a-catheter would have solved the problem, but the nurses knew that Dr. Lawrence did not typically use chemo ports for his melanoma patients.

A port is a plastic or metal disc that is surgically implanted just beneath the skin. A catheter, or soft, thin tube, then connects the port into a vein. Medicines and saline solution can be given through a special needle attached directly to the port. Blood can also be drawn from the port.

Finally, our clinical trial coordinator, Marguerite, stepped in and said, "Enough is enough. We are being cruel to this man. He has been more than patient with US! We have jabbed him 13 times today. I am going to see Dr. Lawrence right now to get an order for a port."

The nurses reported to us that Marguerite marched down to Dr. Lawrence's office and appealed to him that he put in an order for a port implantation. The surgery was done on the very next visit and John was able to use it from then on. John referred to Marguerite as one of his "angels." It takes a village of caregivers when dealing with cancer!

—⁓—

Thanksgiving, 2008
Greetings!
The night of November 4 was among the most memorable and emotional nights I have had in a long time. For the first time since the 1960 election, when I was twelve years old, I was excited

about a candidate who celebrated the audacity of hope and the shared experience of the collective dreams coming true for individuals, numerous groups, and our nation as a whole. Whether you were for McCain or Obama, the culmination of the long political campaign was one that will not soon be forgotten!

I am sure that all of us are at a different place from where we were a year ago ... for innumerable reasons. The frustrations of a downward spiraling economy will have its influence on all of us ... even if we haven't been personally touched yet. Although we know there is hope with the new administrations, both on the state and national levels, we also know that the worst is still ahead of us and that the impact will be difficult for all of us and devastating for many. Our own school district has weathered difficult budgets since 2001 ... but the months ahead, if the pundits are correct, could be the toughest yet.

This has been so true in my own family with my son, Chris, who was recently made a vice president in his company. That was the good news ... the bad news is that he works for the Bank of Wachovia in North Carolina, and he knows that the "writing is on the wall" for job security. He and so many others will be touched by this national crisis ... but, somehow, he and hopefully, most of those affected will get through it.

Many of us are facing problems that may seem overwhelming and even unfair. I learned a long time ago that life is not fair; life is what it is at any given moment. There is happiness, sadness, and every emotion between them. However, I also learned that we can wallow in our sadness or we can "choose our attitude," hold onto our dreams, and maintain our optimism no matter what! We started our administrators' retreat this year with a real dose of what is ahead for education via the new demands from the state and the reality of still diminished resources. At that time, we committed ourselves and our schools to an optimistic course ... because, above all else, education is a profession of optimism.

We all have heroes growing up, and one of mine that you don't hear much about anymore is Helen Keller, who was both blind and deaf, but who had a mind and heart that pained to be set loose! Miraculously, Annie Sullivan came into Helen's life and the world was made a better place. Helen Keller went on to become an author and public speaker. She even wrote a book entitled, "Optimism," in which she wrote, "No pessimist ever discovered the secret of the stars, or sailed to an uncharted land, or opened a new heaven to the human spirit." Later she defined "optimism" by saying that, "Optimism is the faith that leads to achievement. Nothing can be done without hope and confidence." What wise words!

I always have been a dreamer and I have encouraged my own children, my students, and anyone I know to be dreamers too! This year, more than ever though, I am learning just how important it is to be optimistic about the future ... not just on the national level, or the state level, or the district level, but on a very personal level. I have very mixed feelings about retiring from the honor of being Whitman-Hanson's superintendent, but I am very optimistic about the district's future under the leadership of Ruth

Whitner. Working with our committed and dedicated staff, Ruth will take the best of what we have and over time, make it even better. I go on to a new challenge at Cardinal Spellman, not because it was part of a grand master plan or dream, but because I feel it is a natural next step. I will bring them the best of what I have learned in public education, which I treasure, and return to my roots to give back to a place that meant a great deal to me growing up.

The same day I accepted the position at Spellman, I received a phone call from a doctor who bluntly told me that I had cancer. I know that many of us, personally, or someone we love, have had that same devastating call. I just couldn't believe that I would face a high and low of such magnitude on the same day. I told the surgeon I would be his best patient and that I would do whatever it took to get better. This commitment hasn't changed over the past six months, although the doctors, the hospitals, the treatments, and the prognosis have. Now, more than ever, I have had to learn to practice what I preach—and not just dream, but to really commit myself to the spirit of optimism and the miraculous power of prayers, positive thoughts/strong karma (whatever you may call it), and decide that I will be optimistic and positive about this challenge. In spite of a dip in emotions here and there, I can honestly say I am more optimistic and feel stronger than I have felt in a long time. Thank you! Thank you for that gift!

I have much to be thankful for this Thanksgiving! In fact, I believe we all should stop and think about how a positive attitude

and an optimistic embrace of life's challenges
and gifts will get us through whatever faces
us in the months ahead. I am thankful for an
amazingly supportive wife and family. (With
three grandchildren now, I can really understand
why so many grandparents are obnoxious about
seeing the future through their offspring!) I also
have a phenomenal number of colleagues, friends,
and well-wishers who have earnestly propelled me
to function above the problems and to embrace the
challenge to choose to get better. I thank all of you
for that. Your thoughtfulness and prayers humble
me. I wish you and those you love a very special
Thanksgiving and a time to reflect on the past
year and a time to be committed to be optimistic
and strong throughout the year ahead.

In my letters I often refer to the thoughts
that have moved me in the lyrics of a song or a
line of poetry that has touched me. My daughter,
Julie, and I have a special love for a medley of
"Somewhere Over the Rainbow" and "What a
Wonderful World" by the late Hawaiian singer, Iz.
In fact, you can hear the song on YouTube under
"Iz." Somehow, as I think about optimism and
Thanksgiving this year, the words of the song and
Iz's special rendition mean more than ever.

In the meantime, I am more excited about the
future than ever, nationally and locally. What a
nation we live in! In spite of all of our challenges,
we live "in a wonderful world" where "dreams really
do come true;" I know mine have!

Thanks for all you do every day!
John

—m—

John often mentioned our children in his letters to the staff of Whitman-Hanson because they had attended schools in the district. Many on the staff knew them before they knew John other than in his role as a parent.

4

The Holidays 2008

I can still hear the bell!
—John McEwan

O ne of our holiday rituals was to put together a letter to be sent out to friends and family that we did not see often. In 2008, the year John was diagnosed, part of our letter reflected our understanding of John's cancer at the start.

—⁂—

Christmas, 2008
Holiday greetings!
This has been a year of dramatic highs and lows for the McEwans.

Our trip to Disney World in February was particularly memorable because we were the Grand Marshalls of Main Street's midday parade in the Magic Kingdom. John and I had a great time waving at the guests as if we were celebrities. Later that same week, on my real leap year birthday, John, Heather, Julie, and Chris surprised me with a birthday/retirement party. They had invited childhood friends and neighbors, my college roommate, Shaw's colleagues, as well as extended family and friends. What a happy occasion to celebrate!

In April, John decided to retire from public education at the end of the 2008-2009 school year. In May, he was asked if he would consider becoming the first lay president of his high school alma mater after retirement. He said he was looking for flexibility in whatever he did after he retired. They agreed to all of his conditions. Later that same day, John had an appointment with a dermatologist to check out a lump on his head. The doctor confirmed the dreaded diagnosis of melanoma, thought to be in the early stages.

Surgery in June to remove the tumor was successful and pathological lab tests confirmed that there was no cancer in the satellite tissue or lymph nodes. We were forewarned that it could metastasize microscopically anywhere in his body. An immunotherapy treatment was scheduled for late August. We enjoyed a Labor Day weekend trip to Disney with Julie, Heather, and her family. Seeing Disney through the eyes of a twenty-month-old and three-and-a-half-year-old was magical. John started treatments the day after we returned.

After two five-day weeks of immunotherapy, John was experiencing pain in his leg. On the same day that Chris's wife, Liz, gave birth to our third grandchild, Maxwell John, John was told that the cancer had metastasized in three different areas of his body. The doctor then ordered two five-day weeks of radiation to prevent the cancer from growing further and to shrink the existing tumor.

Since then, John has been participating in a clinical trial of a very promising drug manufactured by Novartis. So far, John has suffered no side effects, his energy levels have returned to almost normal, his pain has diminished, and he is back at work.

Throughout this entire ordeal, all of us have remained optimistic. We feel blessed with the quality of the medical care John continues to receive and the empathy in which it is given. There are many lonely moments when a family lives with cancer, but there are many blessings that come from family and friends who recognize the need to make the most of each day that we have together. We have deeply appreciated the prayers, cards, e-mails, and positive thoughts sent our way.

As we celebrate this holiday season, we look forward to the New Year with optimism that we will enjoy every day that we have with each other, our children, our grandchildren, and our circle of supportive friends and family. Through the miracle of prayer and new medicine, John and I will enjoy the holiday season this year in good spirits and we will have even more to celebrate next year at this time.

May you all make the most of this season and the joys that it holds for each of us.

Best wishes,

Margaret and John

The federal government approves how a clinical trial will be conducted. Hospitals and staff must be approved to administer the clinical trials and there must be strict adherence to every aspect of the administration of the trial. The patient must sign a contract, in the presence of his physician, indicating that he understands the terms of the contract and the risks associated with the treatment.

The time required for this first clinical trial was particularly demanding for the patient. It was designed to be three four-week cycles; the drug would be administered twice a week for three weeks and then there would be a week off between cycles that sometimes was needed for scan appointments. The "short" day of drug administration lasted a minimum of four hours; the "long" day could run between ten to twelve hours because of the time required to draw blood samples, wait for lab results, wait for the pharmacy to formulate the drug after the lab results were back, administration of the drug and then the wait for vitals to be taken a specified amount of time after the completion of the IV.

While John was on this first clinical trial, he had a male nurse, Brian, who administered his intravenous treatments. He and John established a very friendly rapport. Brian teased John about how committed he was to doing work while he was receiving treatments. We would bring in John's laptop so that he could conduct business while we were confined to help pass the time. He would respond to e-mails and often dictate the longer e-mails to me so that he would not get behind in his work. Each room was equipped with a television which provided a break if we chose to watch daytime television. We also could watch DVDs on John's laptop.

On one occasion, weathermen had predicted a severe snowstorm for the following day. Calling off school entailed sending a notification out to the district staff, parents, and bus companies so that schedules could be adjusted.

Whitman-Hanson had a reverse phone call system set up so that each student's family was directly notified. The superintendent recorded this message remotely. John said to Brian, "I want to give you a heads up that I need to record a message to call off school tomorrow because of the predicted snowstorm. Would you mind if I had a couple of uninterrupted minutes in the room to do this?" Brian said, "Of course," and left the room closing the door behind him. A few minutes later Brian peeked in the small window to the room and pantomimed hanging up a phone. John signaled thumbs up. Brian walked back into the room and asked, "Are you off the air? Can we get back to the business at hand?"

—⚞—

Excerpt from Christmas Letter to Whitman-Hanson Staff

December 17, 2008
Holiday Greetings!
It really is "the most wonderful time of the year!"
     As we grow older, I have surmised that we often become cynical and more convinced that if we can't see it, it doesn't exist and the sooner our children understand that concept the sooner they will truly grow up. What a shame! We live in a world that is faced with horribly devastating wars, incomprehensible economic challenges, terrifying worldwide diseases, and news stories that seem unfair and unexplainable. We must be able to instill in our children and <u>ourselves</u> the image of a world where there is endless peace, sufficient resources for everyone, cures for diseases and the BELIEF that we can't always comprehend why some things appear unfair or unexplainable ... sometimes things just happen.

I contend that now, more than ever, we must rely on simple BELIEFS, in order to make sense of our lives and the work, in spite of whatever challenges we face as individuals or as a collective humanity. To BELIEVE is a daunting concept that is supported by trust, faith, and a positive outlook through an imagination that is not dependent on facts but on an intuitive conviction that there is more to life than what can be seen, heard, touched, smelled, or tasted. Life is not finite; it is infinite and only limited by our imagination and our ability to BELIEVE.

Christmas, Hanukkah, Kwanza, New Year's ... the holiday season, as a whole, is a time for reflection and resolutions. This year, I ask you to check your own personal barometer regarding what you truly BELIEVE in and how clearly you can still hear the "bell" that was the first gift of Christmas in "The Polar Express." It's not too late to rekindle the amazing power of BELIEF and what it can do to make sense and bring peace to your life and to those who you hold dear. "The Polar Express" is about faith and the power of imagination to sustain faith. It's also about the desire to reside in a world where magic can happen, the kind of world we all believe in as children, but one that disappears as we grow older.

This year has been one of the most challenging years of my life. I am sure that many of you are facing your own personal challenges too as you read this letter. Throughout my life, there have been many times that I have faced uphill battles and beat the odds. I have very strong BELIEFS: some involve religious faith and miracles, but I have convictions too. I BELIEVE in the fundamental goodness of all people and the collective need for all of us to imagine a world that is better than the one we now experience, and the need to keep that vision always in our sights. BELIEVING is truly more powerful than seeing!

I still hear the bell ... and I hope that we all will work hard to keep our imaginations alive and well and to cherish our childlike BELIEFS in Santa Claus, like Virginia O'Hanlon and the boy in "The Polar Express." If you see the film sometime in the future, it ends with a beautiful song, "Believe," sung by Josh Groban.

In the meantime, I enthusiastically want to thank you for all your support and prayers this past year and I humbly ask that you to continue to send them this way in the year ahead. I really do BELIEVE! I also want to wish you and those you love a wonderful holiday season and a year filled with laughter, love and the ability to hear the sound of the bell!

John

5

Interleukin-2

Life is not fair but it is what it is.
—John McEwan

———✺———

January 26, 2009

Dear Family and Friends:

Today we got the results from John's scans of last week, and the news was not all bad ... but not all good, either. However, we still have a great deal of hope that we are going to beat this thing.

The doctor feels that the clinical trial that John has been participating in for the last three months has not stabilized the progress of the cancer. The good news is that there is no cancer in the brain and no new sites can be seen. Unfortunately, some of the spots on the sites that they had seen on the earlier scans have gotten larger. The doctor feels that John continues to look good, and his energy and spirits have been exceptional, but he wants to get more aggressive at this point.

The doctor has given John a choice again of waiting for a new clinical trial or moving aggressively to an immunotherapy treatment called Interleukin-2. This had been mentioned to us on many occasions, and we knew at some point that John would probably undergo this treatment. They have been administering this treatment for many years at Mass General, and John's oncologist, Dr. Lawrence, personally has overseen this treatment for fifteen years. He is considered highly qualified, in fact only one of three doctors in New England who can oversee this treatment. We feel John is in very good hands and the doctor still is very hopeful that we will find a way to beat this.

The main drawback to the treatment is that John will have to face significant side effects ... so much so that he has to be hospitalized throughout the treatment. There are a wide variety of side effects inducing sepsis: intense fatigue, flu-like symptoms, low blood pressure, and weight gain due to fluid retention. He will be in the hospital receiving the treatment every eight hours for five days. He will have two days more in the hospital and then be released for a week. He will then return for a second round of treatments on the same time line.

John wanted to start as early as possible, so he will be admitted next Monday, February 2, for the first round. He will not be able to work during these treatments and will probably miss a total of five to six weeks of work. One month after the treatment ends, John will undergo a scan to see what effect the treatment has had. There have been cases (only five to ten percent) where the patient has gone into total remission. If, in fact, the treatment is helping to reduce the cancer sites, but has not been completely successful, he can undergo an additional round of treatments in the future.

We are surprised and disappointed by today's news. We were both optimistic that John would be able to continue on the clinical trial, but we are also realistic enough to know that he is still experiencing pain and that the cancer is still present.

The doctor has reassured us that there are patients who have had much more advanced cases than John's present condition and have had very successful results.

As always, we appreciate your support and we ask that you continue to keep us in your prayers as we face this next phase of our journey.

With continued optimism and hope,

Margaret and John

With the exception of not sharing John's life expectancy in the beginning, we were always very direct with our adult children about his illness and how he was responding to treatments. We respected that each of them would cope in their own way.

Our elder daughter was married and had two young children who had a close relationship with John. To us, she appeared to transfer her anxiety about John's health by devoting a lot of time to managing her children's fears and concerns. Our son was married and lived out of state, so he was coping with the guilt of not being more readily available to us. He stayed in touch by phone or Skype, and he made more efforts to come home for visits than he may have if John had not been ill. We also made efforts to visit them when we could. Our younger daughter, Julie, was a guidance counselor. She had suffered a significant loss as a young adult that led her to pursue a master's degree with a special emphasis on grief counseling. Julie was very sensitive to her siblings and how they were dealing with John's illness. She did not try to impose on them unless they asked for advice, particularly as it related to their interactions with their own children. Naturally, she would ask her father how he was doing or feeling. But she would also be one of the few who would ask how I was handling things. She always was an exceptionally good solicitor and listener.

February 11, 2009

Dear Family and Friends:

As many of you know, our daughter, Julie, volunteers to help kids cope with the loss of a parent or sibling. During one weekly session, the children shared a thought with her that she shared with me. She said, "The children tell me that there is a sound to hope; sometimes it is soft and sometimes it is loud but it is always there." This week the volume was turned down for us. I pray that we can hear it loudly again.

There was a very good reason that John was hospitalized for the Interleukin-2. It is an immunotherapy treatment designed to boost up the immune system; however, it is aggressive and the side effects are extreme. Although 14 doses can be given, only the number of treatments that an individual can tolerate is administered. There is no correlation between the number of treatments received and the ultimate success of the treatment.

John received eight treatments out of the possible 14. The first three days John experienced some side effects, but all seemed to be going very well. On the fourth day, his blood pressure dropped significantly, which was a direct result of the fluid that built up in his body. This is an anticipated side effect, but when the pressure remains low, even with medication, the treatment has to be suspended. Though we understood that everything was going as expected, we were disappointed that John could not receive all of the treatments.

But that was Thursday.

Unfortunately, Friday evening John's kidneys showed stress. Although this was also a common side effect, it was slightly unusual because he had not received treatments for two days. By Friday night, John was very confused and disoriented—another known side effect. He did not know where he was or what was happening to him. This was a very scary experience for him and very hard to witness. Saturday was a very difficult day. By Sunday, he improved, but certainly was not stable enough physically or mentally to come home. Fortunately, by Monday he showed even greater improvement, so he was discharged Tuesday.

It bears repeating that all of the side effects were directly related to the Interleukin-2 treatments and all of the side effects will clear over the next week.

John is very happy to be home and resting comfortably. He has very little appetite and sleeps a lot. Luckily, he is no longer confused or disoriented.

Still, the difficult parts of this treatment plan lie ahead. John is expected to return to the hospital on Tuesday, February 17, for the second round of treatments. Needless to say, this is a very challenging decision for him to have to make. I will support him no matter what he decides but I would like to have him complete this second round, if he possibly can.

As always thank you for your continued support and prayers. They have certainly helped our entire family through this challenging time.

Love,

Margaret

——✦——

On the Friday night of the first week, after I had left the hospital, John convinced his nurse that he needed to talk to me for reassurance. The call came just as I was arriving home from the hospital.

The nurse handed off the phone to John who was talking very fast and with slightly slurred speech. He said, "Margaret, I am so disappointed in you. I thought you loved me. I cannot believe that you are leaving me in the hospital and allowing the staff to mistreat me in this way."

He clearly was frightened and did not understand how compromised he had become as a result of this treatment. I knew that these were symptoms of temporary psychosis, but it was very sad for me not knowing whether he would ever "come to his senses."

When the nurse overheard what he was saying, she quickly took the phone away from him and apologized to me. She reassured me that he was not responsible for what he was saying. Naturally, I cried, but I pulled myself together before I entered my house where my children were expecting me for dinner. I was shaken when I came into the house and the kids knew something was wrong. I was forced to tell them about the phone call. They too were very empathetic because they had witnessed his behavior during a visit earlier in the week and realized that he was just not himself.

As I reflect on the many hospitalizations that John experienced during his cancer journey, this one stands out. Throughout his entire life, John had met so many challenges with a firm commitment that he would "get through it." He always said, "Life is not fair, but it is what it is." A side effect of this treatment had caused him to become psychotic. How could he fight back when he had lost contact with reality?

—⁂—

February 24, 2009
        Dear Family and Friends:
        John was discharged yesterday from his second series of Interleukin-2 treatments. From the beginning, we were told that the cumulative effect of this very aggressive treatment would often cause the second week of treatments to be more difficult to endure than the first. We also were cautioned that since John had received eight treatments the first time, he would likely only be able to tolerate four treatments this time. Knowing this made it that much more difficult to face the second hospitalization.
        However, John agreed that if he was going to attempt to control or possibly eliminate this disease, he was going to have to have as many treatments administered as possible.
        As you all know (and now his doctor knows), John is a man of surprises! Not only did he receive nine treatments this time, he tolerated them better

than he tolerated the first round! John left both his doctor and nurses shaking their heads. Of course, he did experience side effects, the most annoying of which was itchy skin. (Funny how it is always the little things that can drive you crazy.) Throughout the week, we kept waiting for the longer-lasting, more serious side effects to kick in. They just didn't.

John came home yesterday on schedule and is resting comfortably. He is very tired, but his mind is alert. He has even been able to keep up with his e-mails and conducted some schoolwork throughout his hospital stay. We expect that he will get stronger each day.

We would be remiss if we did not recognize the extraordinary nursing and medical care John received throughout his hospital stay. The medical staff promised that they would get us through this, but they did more than that: They offered truly professional and compassionate care during some very difficult days. We thank God that there are people in this world who have the desire and the gift of caring for fellow human beings during some of their most challenging and complicated health conditions. Even people from the clinical study from his previous treatment came to visit John. We have been truly blessed by each of them coming into our lives.

And of course our children, their spouses, and our grandchildren have been such a source of strength and hope for us. They are the reason that gives purpose to this difficult journey. If hope has a sound, our family is its face.

So now the "patience" part of the journey begins. John's PET scan is scheduled for March

23. We will know on March 25 what the results of
this treatment have been. We hope that the treatment will curb the growth of the cancer sites. In
five to ten percent of the cases, the cancer is
even eliminated. Certainly positive results will
be welcomed, but we both agree that if they were
not the results we hope for, at least we will have
tried this option. We will then look for another
treatment.

Again, God has offered us the blessing of a
wonderful diversion as we wait. Chris, his wife,
Liz, and Maxwell John will be coming home for two
weeks during March for Maxwell's christening. We
are all so looking forward to celebrating this
happy occasion with our family.

Thank you all again for your continued support
and prayers. You have all contributed to the volume
of hope. We sincerely value all of you in our lives.

Love,

Margaret and John

In retrospect, one of the hardest chapters in our journey
was the week between the Interleukin-2 treatments. I had
taken up the offer from John's friend, Jack, to accompany
me to the hospital to assist in getting John home. I knew
John would not be happy that I had done this because he did
not want people outside of our immediate family to know
exactly how sick he was. But this time I needed the help.

When John arrived home, he walked into the house,
sat down on the couch and emphatically pronounced, "I am
not going back for the second round of treatments." Clearly
I understood why he would not want to go but I pleaded
with him, "Just give it a few days before you finalize your

decision." I knew the time would come when he simply could not subject himself to treatment or that his body would not be able to fight any longer, but I really wanted him to try to do this.

A day later the oncology nurse called to check on how John was doing at home. I told her that he did not want to return. She agreed that I should give it some time to let him work it out. I respected the fact that he was the one undergoing the treatments, but I also knew that in the future, he might regret not having completed the full cycle.

About two days later, John reluctantly agreed to go for the second round of treatments. I cried when he told me. In making the decision he said, "I am doing this for you, not for me."

During the time at home, there were several people who called to ask if they could stop by for a visit. John was reluctant to have visitors because he always took on the responsibility for making conversation. From the visitors' perspective, cancer adds a sense of urgency that otherwise might be put off.

John had one sister and four brothers. His sister and a brother telephoned to ask if they could visit John while he was at home recuperating. The siblings did not see each other often, but they loved each other and knew that John, the oldest sibling in the family, was gravely ill. He finally agreed to have them come but I did have to encourage them to keep the visit brief because I could see that John was having a hard time keeping up with the conversation.

After recuperating at home for several days, the time came to return to the hospital for the next round of treatments. As we walked into the hospital, John refused to use a wheelchair. He stubbornly insisted on walking in under his own power dejectedly dragging his laptop with him. He looked like a sad puppy dog! I felt so badly for him, but I was pleased that he had agreed to go for the second round.

The second week of treatments was scheduled right around Valentine's Day. After John was released from the hospital, our son Chris was home for a visit. Chris relayed a conversation that he had had with his father. He said that John told him, "The decision to return to the hospital was my Valentine to your mother." This was the most selfless gift of love I had ever received.

6

Courage and Determination: a Trip to China

*When the world says, "Give up," Hope
whispers, "Try it one more time."*
—Anonymous

March 23, 2009

Dear Friends and Family:

The volume of hope has been turned up in a big way today. Earlier today, John had the PET scan that would determine whether or not the Interleukin-2 treatment had any effect. Unexpectedly, we got the results later this afternoon. We are very happy with the news.

The nurse practitioner told us that John shows significant response to Interleukin-2. There has been shrinkage of the cancerous lesions; with these results they expect that the lesions will continue to get smaller. She said that she and the doctor agreed that they could not sit on this good news until tomorrow; they wanted to share it with us right away.

We know we aren't out of the woods yet, but we are taking this as a major blessing in our lives. What made it even more special was that we were both home to receive the phone call and we were able to share the good news directly with Julie, Heather, and Chris right away.

We have a scheduled appointment with the doctor on Thursday and he will tell us what is next. We expect that John will go in for another PET scan in another month to—hopefully—see more positive results. In the meantime, we are going to enjoy this month of improving results. John has been feeling better overall. He still gets fatigued and the itchiness in his body has not gone away, but there has been a significant reduction in his pain. He is working almost on a full-time schedule and he feels a little stronger every day.

In just three and a half weeks, we are fulfilling one of John's dreams to lead a group, many of them educators, to China. Seventy-four adults are headed to Beijing, Xi'an, and Shanghai.

We certainly appreciate what the medical field has been able to provide to John. But, just as important to us has been the continued support and prayers from all of you. It has made a difference in how we, as a family, have been able to cope with the emotional ups and downs of this cancer journey. We thank each of you for your part in this journey.

With love and gratitude,
Margaret and John

—〰—

John was very involved in introducing a global exchange program with schools in China into the Whitman-Hanson Regional School District. In 2006, he made his first trip to China with a group of educators and wanted to make a return trip with adults from the community to expose them to the benefits of what a global education could provide for students. When John offered the trip for adults, he was hoping for 12 people to sign up. In the end, 74 people took advantage of the opportunity.

Throughout the fall, as John consulted with Dr. Lawrence about which treatments he might be eligible for, he would ask the doctor if he thought the trip to China was realistic. At every step along the way, Dr. Lawrence told John he thought he would be able to lead the group.

When the time came for the discussion about the required hospitalization and the side effects from Interleukin-2, John again asked Dr. Lawrence if he really thought he should find someone else to take his place to lead the group to China in April. Dr. Lawrence reiterated that if he could start the treatment in early February, he believed John would be able to make the journey. John laughed and said, "You do not owe me a trip to China." Dr. Lawrence replied, "I feel I do. With all that you have gone through with Interferon treatments, radiation, and the first clinical trial, I really want you to be able to make this trip."

The following letter was written by John to his staff and is offered to give you insight into his character. No matter what role a person had within a school community, John took every opportunity he could to thank people for their contribution to each student's success. This letter demonstrates some self-reflections as he had cancer treatments and that all of us achieve our personal goals with help from others.

May 8, 2009
E-mail to all District Staff
Subject: Appreciation
Good morning!

I have not found the appropriate card to send everyone, but I do know what sentiment I would want to communicate during Appreciation Week this year. I truly know what teachers, nurses, and support staffs do to make our schools work as effectively as they do. Our profession, more than any other, is committed to helping children reach their full potential academically, physically, and emotionally. We teach kids to be contributing citizens; hardworking individuals who, hopefully, feel good about themselves and the world around them. This is a huge undertaking that we partner with parents and the community as a whole. As with all of us, we want them to be optimistic about their futures and their talents but also realistic about their limitations and challenges.

I have had a plaque on my desk for over 30 years that is called "The Essence of Teaching." It reads, "What nobler profession than to touch the next generation—to see children hold your understanding in their eyes, your hope in their lives, your world in their hands. In their success you find your own and so to them you give your all." That is the message I would put in a greeting card!

Thanks for all you do and continue to do every day for the children of Hanson and Whitman.

Have a great day, and Happy Mother's Day!
John

As the Superintendent of Schools, John felt the most important annual event in the community was graduation. Probably because of John's own family history, he felt very strongly that all students should be given the opportunity to earn a high school diploma by offering the right environment for them to learn and achieve this goal. He knew that some students had faced difficult life circumstances that often stood in the way of earning a diploma.

Although he always was proud of the students who were able to succeed in a traditional school environment, he was even more professionally gratified by the success of the students who attended an alternative school or community school program where they could earn a high school diploma. He wished it could have been an option for his own sister and brothers. John gave the following graduation speech at the alternative school graduation exercises in 2009, the year John retired from public education and one year after his cancer diagnosis.

—m—

June 2009
Excerpt from the Whitman-Hanson Community School Graduation Speech

An unknown author once said, "When the world says, 'Give up,' Hope whispers, 'Try it one more time.'" Today is clear witness to the truth, that no matter what your situation or challenge was in the way to your high school diploma, someone somewhere, gave you hope and whispered to you, "Try it one more time."

I come from a family of six. I have four brothers and one sister. We are all well over forty, and we all have chosen a variety of paths for our life's work. Believe it or not three of us received a high school diploma and three of us never graduated from high school, and yet we all came from the same home. During our high school years, things were a challenge for all of us for different reasons, and we still talk today about that high school diploma and its impact on our future lives.

Three of us had teachers or friends who helped us along the way to focus on that education in order to earn our diplomas. Three of us either did not have that support or did not accept the encouragement or support that was offered. To this day, they still regret that they did not receive a high school diploma, and for a variety of personal reasons they have been too busy with other things to go back and reach that goal.

I am glad that, in spite of any challenges you faced whether they were personal, financial, and educational, or whatever else they may have been, that you made the sacrifices to get your diploma today. No matter what happens throughout your lives, I hope you can look back and say, "No regrets!"

Your diploma today symbolizes that you have been hopeful; that you have been willing to make sacrifices and that you will continue to live a life with no regrets. Make sure that you continue to listen to the people who truly care for you and that you thank them along the way for their support. None of us succeeds alone. Receiving your diploma today is a real foundation for your future success.

7

Success Means You Get to Do It Again

Everything will be all right in the end.
If it isn't all right, it is not yet the end.
—Patel, character from *The Best Exotic Marigold Hotel*

As the school year was winding down, John knew he would face another set of Interleukin-2 treatments at the beginning of the summer. True to his nature, John did not want to brood over what was coming next, so we squeezed in a quick getaway to New York City to see some Broadway shows. We actually left from his office on his last official day of work at Whitman-Hanson and headed directly to the train station to take a late afternoon train to New York City. We spent the weekend going to shows and museums, one of John's favorite getaways.

John always was better at living in the moment than I was. As we spent this precious time together, I distinctly remember becoming emotionally overwhelmed at one point about what we had to face when we returned home. John reassured me that we all only have the gift of each day. We had to make the most of the time we were given and not worry about tomorrow.

As testimony to the roller coaster ride of our cancer journey, I remember coming home on the train from New York and watching Fourth of July fireworks as we rode through the Connecticut coastline. Somehow, it gave us a sense of joyous celebration—for the moment. It was an image and feeling that I will never forget ... always celebrate life ... when you can!

—⁄⁄⁄—

June 29, 2009

Dear Family and Friends:

On Thursday of last week John underwent a brain scan (an MRI), a PET scan, and a CT scan. We have just returned from the doctor's consultation visit and the news is that there are no new cancer sites. There is no melanoma in the brain or in the bone tissue. (If it had occurred in the brain, we understand that he probably would not have qualified for the next round of treatments in early July.) The doctor said the goal for the second round of Interleukin-2 treatments is not simply to slow or arrest the growth of the cancer sites but to eliminate all of them. The doctor continues to be very optimistic because of John's response the first time.

This round of treatments will follow the same routine that John underwent in February. He will receive infusions up to three times per day for five consecutive days as long as his body can tolerate it. He will stay two days longer in the hospital, come home for a week, and then go back in for another five days of treatments and two days recuperation.

The side effects, as we know, can vary for each person, each time he receives treatments ... so we have no way of knowing what the side effects will be or how long they will last. At least we have some idea of how John reacted to the treatments.

John is once again going in with a very positive attitude. Right now, he feels well; he takes Tylenol for pain in his back and the site of his skin graft, and his energy level is very high. We know that he will not feel well for at least six weeks after the treatment, but it will be well worth the investment of time and ill health if he can eliminate the cancer. Meanwhile, we have enjoyed a wonderful spring of improving health and high energy.

John will be officially retired from Whitman-Hanson in another two weeks. He plans to start in his new role as President of Cardinal Spellman High School on July first.

The last time I communicated with all of you in March, we expected that John would lead a group of 74 adults to China. He could not walk a flight of stairs three weeks before we left, but three weeks later we walked the Great Wall. This trip demonstrated what medicine, prayers, positive attitude, and sheer determination to achieve dreams can do.

We believe we can achieve our goal of eliminating the cancer and take pleasure in a good quality of life. I will keep you informed on John's response to the treatments. As always, we appreciate your prayers and support as we undergo this next challenging round of treatments.

Gratefully,

Margaret

Throughout our cancer journey, John demonstrated over and over again that he would not allow his illness to define him as a person. The trip to China demonstrated one of his most defiant acts of sheer will and determination to achieve his goal of living life fully with a stage IV cancer diagnosis.

In June 2009, John wrote a reflection of his feelings just days before the anticipated readmission to the hospital for the second round of Interleukin-2 treatments. The following is an excerpt.

—⁓—

Thoughts on Interleukin-2: From a Patient's Point of View by John F. McEwan

From a patient's point of view, the three worst words you can hear are, "You have cancer."

The first step to the road to recovery is the five-word statement, "It is what it is." Clear communication about the nature of the disease from the doctor and realistic acceptance of the prognosis on the part of the patient create an overwhelming bond that will impact the patient's life forever.

I am a sixty-year-old man who has been living with a diagnosis of cancer for the past year and an individual who has learned a great deal about himself, his disease, and Interleukin-2 over that time.

Each patient's background is different and each patient's cancer is different too. There had been no history of cancer on either side of my family. My father died in a fire at the age of 34 and my mother passed away with heart-related problems at the age of 68. My diagnosis of cancer came as a complete surprise when a bump on my head, which I had thought was a fatty tumor, was removed and was later found to be melanoma. The surgeon removed the melanoma and some lymph glands and was optimistic that the cancer had been arrested. Upon a referral to my current oncologist, Dr. Donald Lawrence, the proactive therapy became irrelevant once it was decided that the cancer had metastasized and the message, "You have cancer," resonated in my mind.

I then experienced all of the levels of loss as defined by Elizabeth Kübler-Ross and reflected on her wisdom, "Learn to get in touch with the silence within yourself and know that everything in this life has a purpose, there are no mistakes, no coincidences, all events are blessings given to us to learn from." Beyond the reflection and self-doubt the final process led to the assertion that "It is what it is." In a very short time period, my family and I went through the classic stages enumerated in Kübler-Ross' works:

The shock stage: the initial paralysis at hearing the bad news;

The denial stage: trying to avoid the inevitable;

The anger stage: frustrated outpouring of bottled-up emotion;

The bargaining stage: seeking in vain for a way out;

The depression stage: final realization of the inevitable;

The testing stage: seeking realistic solutions; and

The acceptance stage: finally finding the way forward.*

*This model represents the slightly extended version of the original Kübler-Ross model, which does not explicitly include the shock and testing stages.

The length of the experience of these seven stages lasts differently for each individual but the ultimate outcome is to first reaffirm in your mind that "It is what it is." Then with a sense of real purpose, tinged with a major commitment to hope for the best, the patient needs to collaborate with the physician and say, "I'll do whatever it takes … to get better!"

That is where I am! I have a true realization of faith and hope; I possess a profound sense of what is the medical reality for me and the menu of alternatives available to me. And I have an unwavering commitment to embrace a positive, enthusiastic attitude no matter what emotions or pain I am experiencing at that moment. With that in mind, my wife and I chose to participate in a variety of options including Interferon, radiation, and a clinical study, which seemed at first to be positive, optimistic choices. The first two options did not help and, after three months of the clinical study, when the scans showed that there was no diminishment of the cancer, we were devastated but not defeated.

We knew that the doctor had mentioned that the "big gun," Interleukin-2, was somewhat of a "last resort" and we both knew that it was time to face the "big gun." It took me all of thirty seconds to agree to this awesome decision. In fact, my wife and I had overheard two nurses discussing (in front of us) whether they would ever agree to go through Interleukin-2, knowing the severity and reality of the somewhat unpredictable side effects resulting from the treatment. My response was, "Let's do it. Let's do it as soon as possible." The doctor appeared to be surprised at the quickness

of my decision and then cautioned me that I had
to get through physical tests to see if I was strong
enough to endure the wrath of Interleukin-2: one
was a stress test and the other was a pulmonary
test. In the next few days, I nervously took both
tests and was delighted that I passed them. I may
not have known what I was getting myself into,
but I knew that I was at least going to take a
risk "to beat the odds" of a death sentence from
melanoma, the cancer, "which gives a bad name to
other cancers."

A week later, on February 2, the day after
enjoying the celebration of the Super Bowl with
my family, I was at Mass General and was
admitted to Ellison 14, the floor for challenging
cancers. It was one of the scariest mornings of
my life, but at the same time, one where I felt like
a team member who was falling backward in the
arms of my other team members who would catch
me and make sure that I would not fall.

My wife brought me home for my recovery.
In the hospital, I had been able to be in touch with
work through e-mails and phone calls. I even
negotiated with an attorney about a serious legal
issue related to work. I continued to do these
things from home. In fact, I had a meeting of
my staff in my home less than a week after my
return. Throughout my cancer treatments, I had
a number of goals and projects I still wanted to
do at work. Fortuitously, I had announced my
retirement from public education before I knew I
had cancer, but there were certain goals I still had
that year. Some were very doable ... like reading
to every elementary class in my school district.
Others were more awesome and seemed, at times,

undoable. I constantly asked the doctor about
whether I would be able to lead a trip to China.
Dr. Lawrence was always realistic but he never
discouraged me from being able to take this trip.
Along the way, I continued to communicate with
my fellow travelers and we worked on the fine
details of the trip. I still was profoundly weak and
the flights and responsibility of running the tour
seemed overwhelming. Was I just dealing with
wishful thinking? Would I be one of the patients
who met with some success? Would I get to China?

The next steps were about a month later when
I returned to Mass General for a full set of scans.
It seemed strange to return to the hospital and it
was one of the scarier days of my life, as I drank
the barium, and lay in the machines, ready to
assess my body's progress with the Interleukin-2.
My mind was swimming with cautionary
optimism! My wife and I returned home and
waited for the phone call from the doctor's office
sometime in the next few days. It seemed a long
time but it actually was much sooner than
promised. The nurse practitioner on the phone said
that they were so happy to report great results.
The cancer was not gone but the sites had been
favorably impacted by the Interleukin-2. It was
not over but there was "good news." My wife hung
up the phone, sat on our couch and we fell into
each other's arms … crying.

In a few days, we met with Dr. Lawrence and
his staff and we all were very happy with the news
and the progress. I was still much weakened but I
was also exhilarated, knowing that the treatments
were "beating the odds." I would be able to lead the
trip to China! I would continue to get better and be

able to return to the office. (I never really stopped working in July in order to, hopefully, complete the work begun in February.) In the weeks ahead, I would continue to receive the benefits of the treatment in my system and I would recover much of the muscle loss and weight loss (thirty pounds in two weeks!). All this ... and I would be retiring in June and beginning a new leadership position at a private school in July. There was much on my plate. There were many reasons to choose to do what it takes to get better!

The hardest part of work when I returned was climbing the 43 steps (I have counted them!) to my office. It was excruciating, and I had to "give-in" to the elevator for the first few weeks. I kept thinking that if I was this weak, how could I possibly lead the trip to China in April? The regenerative transformation of the body, not to mention the curative impact of the Interleukin-2, has been amazing! With a small amount of pain medication, and a bit of light exercise, I did begin to get better. I was not 100 percent ... but I was getting better.

Three weeks before I went to China, I couldn't climb the stairs. By the time I got to China, I was able to climb the Great Wall! One of my major goals had been reached in spite of my bout with malignant melanoma and treatment with Interleukin-2. I was able to lead and inspire 74 fellow travelers to appreciate Global Awareness "up close" and hopefully, upon their return home, to foster in their lives an enthusiastic appreciation for the development of twenty-first century skills for their students and our schools. I was more committed than ever to the tenet that educators must prepare children for their futures and not our pasts. The fulfillment of this trip became a concrete example of the fact that dreams, in spite of cancer, can come true!

As I write this paper, I am getting ready to pack my bags to begin the second series of Interleukin-2 at Mass General. I have enjoyed a heartwarming retirement party/reunion that I will never forget. I have heard from friends and former students from the past thirty-seven years. I have left one job and begun the next. I have set short-range and long-range goals for myself, my family, and my work. My bout with cancer has provided me a foundation for my faith and hope, as well as an opportunity to know how much I love people and how much people love me too. My wife and I have said that this has been the worst year and best year of our lives. We have lived with an increased sensitivity about the value and worth of every day and of every human experience. That is an amazing blessing!

Right now, my mind continues to think about my past experiences in the hospital. The challenges of the fear and pain are balanced by the extraordinary support and encouragement of my wife, my family, Dr. Lawrence, and the Mass General medical staff. I constantly say I am glad when I live and where I live ... near Boston. I know there are no guarantees, but I also know that if I don't keep trying, there will be no chance of recovery. Beating the odds the first time made every moment of the Interleukin-2 worthwhile. I have no doubt about that. Who knows what will happen the second time? One way or the other, though, I know that I am in good hands. I am still trusting my team will catch me and ... I am still filled with hope. Most importantly, knowing what I know, if I had it to do all over again ... I would!

Being a patient with a serious health condition is mind-boggling and life changing. Dealing with the decision about whether to face a treatment as unpredictable and awesome as Interleukin-2 is not to be taken lightly. The information pamphlets tell you in black and white what IL-2 is, but they do not tell you how you will feel as you go through it or how it may or may not impact your mind, your spirit, or your relationships with your family. The physicians are supernaturally honest about the "odds" and the side effects. They want the best for each patient, but they have to be realistic in their offerings and honest in their advice. You can be paralyzed by the unknown or enervated by the choice to face the challenge head-on.

Tomorrow, I begin Interleukin-2 again. My attitude is very different now ... not just because I have met with some success, but because I know I have survived and gotten better from the first set of treatments. Some days seemed endless and it was unimaginable that I would actually recover from the pain, the fatigue, the depression, the anger and even the itch ... but I did. My immediate hope is to get through the treatment a week at a time, a day at a time, and even an hour at a time. My long-term hope is to begin my new job and to take a long-planned trip to Greece with my wife and in-laws. We also are planning a family trip to Disney World and another trip with my fellow China travelers to "Behind the Iron Curtain" in the spring. I always will have one more trip to plan. I also am hoping to do more volunteer work and I even plan to return to my old school district to read to each of those elementary classrooms that I put off last school year.

From a patient's point of view, Interleukin-2 has been both a mystery and a miracle. It has brought me the fear of the unknown and the joy of "beating the odds." Even though the odds continue to be humbling, I face the next series of treatments with determination and trust. For my family and me IT WAS WORTH EVERYTHING ... especially, because we were not successful with other treatments. I am very thankful to Dr. Lawrence, to his staff and to the dedicated nurses and technicians of the Massachusetts General Hospital. I have learned to accept my cancer and, working with the experts, as well as learning from Kübler-Ross, I have been able to find "the way forward." I have been able to discover that making even risky choices about your future is much better than accepting defeat. Interleukin-2 may be a difficult choice at an extremely challenging time in your life ... but it was the right choice for me.

Tomorrow I will find out what lies around the next turn of that roller coaster ride. Whatever it brings, I am glad that I have chosen this path to recovery.

———

July 13, 2009

Dear Family and Friends:

John came home today on schedule from his first in the second series of Interleukin-2 treatments. He is resting fairly comfortably.

John received 10 out of a possible 14 treatments

over five days. In February, he received eight
treatments the first week and nine treatments the
second week. There is no magic number; the number
of doses depends on how each person's body reacts
to the treatments. They told us that John might
only be able to tolerate as few as four treatments this time since this was his second regimen.
Although he was very uncomfortable for the last
two days of treatments, and he continues to feel
generally weak and very tired, he did not suffer
any extreme side effects. The doctor and nurses
were pleased with his response to this round of
treatments. He continues to receive excellent care
and compassionate support from the staff at Mass
General Hospital.

We are delighted that he can rest and recover
during beautiful weather; it does help the spirits.
He actually looks better than he did either of the
previous two times and he has started to lose some
of the 20 pounds of water weight that he gained
this past week. As you can imagine, it is very
difficult to face the week of recovery and then
another round of treatments, but we still remain
very optimistic that we can rid his body of cancer
through these treatments. We can only hope and
pray that he does as well during the next round.

Thank you for your continued support and
prayers.

Love,

Margaret

———〜〰〜———

Always in a planning mode, John and I had wanted to
better utilize the space we had in our house by eliminating
one bedroom and replacing it with a second full bath and

walk-in closet to create a master suite. John decided that the perfect time for us to undergo this renovation would be during the summer, while he was in the hospital receiving Interleukin-2 treatments. I argued, "John, this might work for you but it is going to create additional stress for me." He assured me that, "We know what we are facing with the Interleukin treatments." Exasperated I said, "My point exactly!" He was quick to add that, "It will be the perfect time to be working on something constructive. It will give me something else to focus on while I am in the hospital and then recovering at home."

Well, you know who won that argument? Throughout John's hospital stay for the second round of Interleukin-2 treatments, I carried in samples of paint chips and product, etc. I tried to convince him that a manufactured solid surface would work just fine on the vanity but he insisted on granite. Let me tell you, even small granite samples are heavy. The nurses, nurses' assistants, and even the maintenance staff marveled at John's interest and enthusiasm for such a project while being hospitalized.

—⟋⟍⟍—

July 27, 2009

Dear Family and Friends:

John and I reached another milestone this weekend. He finished his second week of Interleukin-2 treatments, and we couldn't be more relieved.

As I told you all in the last e-mail, he had ten treatments during the first week of this round and he handled them pretty well. The week home between treatments was so much better than we had anticipated. He was able to eat, climb stairs, and actually go out for a few short rides to do errands. On the Sunday before he was readmitted, we even went to see the new Harry Potter movie. All seemed to be going well.

On Sunday, July 19, we were instructed to call for the time of admission on Monday morning. They said that John was scheduled but they weren't sure if they were going to have a bed for him. When we called back Monday, they still were working on his admission. Finally, we were called and told to be in as soon as possible. This was how our week of treatments started, which was a preview to how the week would go.

After receiving the two scheduled treatments on Monday, overnight John's electrolytes were out of balance and his blood pressure plummeted. All expected side effects of Interleukin-2, but each time it happened, he would have to be treated with medicine to counteract the side effects. The nursing staff administered the ordered doses of medication to bring his electrolyte levels within a normal range and to lower his blood pressure, but he was not showing an adequate response. Tuesday, he received no treatments and was told there was a possibility that he might have to be admitted to the Intensive Care Unit.

By the end of the week, he was told two more times that he might have to be admitted to the ICU and, in the end, he only received four treatments. Considering this was John's fourth week of Interleukin-2 treatments, this was not surprising to the doctor, the nursing staff, or to me, but it was disappointing. By the end of the week, we were both relieved that the pressure of anticipating treatments was over. He was finally released on Sunday in the early afternoon.

We have been anxiously anticipating this hospitalization since March and the burden and risks of having these treatments is finally over.

Now, we will have to wait until the end of August to have scans done to find out the results of these 14 additional treatments. We have been told repeatedly that the number of treatments administered is totally dependent on the body's ability to accept the treatments. When each individual has reached his maximum point of endurance, the treatments must stop. We had both arrived at the conclusion that four treatments was enough this time for John. We feel blessed that he had been given the chance to go in for a second round. He is among the fortunate 15 to 20 percent of the population that even responds to the treatments. So his odds are good that he should have a positive response this time, we just don't know if it will be enough to eliminate the melanoma from his body.

We remain optimistic that it will. Whatever the results, we have done what we could to totally rid his body of cancer, at least for the time being. This will not be the end of possible treatments, but to date, there are no other options for complete elimination of melanoma tumors.

We thank you all for your continued support in the cancer journey with us. We are anxious to get on with the routine of life. We treasure each day.

Love,

Margaret

8

Failure Means New Options and a Trip to Greece

What kind of man would live where there is no daring? I don't believe in taking foolish chances, but nothing can be accomplished without taking any chance at all.
—Charles A. Lindbergh

August 26, 2009

Dear Family and Friends:

Today was the follow-up visit with John's oncologist to discuss the results of July's Interleukin-2 treatment. The scan results showed no brain cancer, but the melanoma sites have not been eliminated. In fact, one tumor has shown some slow growth. The fact that he has no brain metastases means he is still treatable, so this is positive news.

The doctor said that given the very slow rate of cancer growth that John is currently experiencing, John could choose to do nothing for a few months in terms of treatment. John does not want to even consider this option. There are two other possible options available.

One is for us to be referred to the National Cancer Institute in Bethesda, Maryland for what is called "Adaptive Cell Transfer." In short, it means that John would have to undergo chemotherapy to eliminate his immune system, then a cell infusion, much like stem cell transplant, and finally another round of Interleukin-2. Obviously, this is a pretty potent and toxic treatment, but their research shows that about 50 percent of the patients go into remission. The doctor challenges this number because only a selective few can undergo this treatment to begin with, but it does offer an option. It would mean hospitalization in Maryland for at least two months. The doctor would like us to visit the National Cancer Institute sometime over the next month so that we can assess their program and they can evaluate John.

The other very promising option would be if John could qualify for a clinical study at Mass General that has shown excellent results during the earliest trials. The new wonder drug is called PLX 4032. Apparently about 50 percent of melanomas have a BRAF protein cell that responds to targeted drug therapies by blocking the growth of the melanoma cells, at least temporarily. If John qualifies, he would require two overnight hospitalizations in the first three weeks of treatment, but otherwise, the drug is taken orally twice a day at home with minimal side effects. The doctor said that people are lining up all over the country to be considered for this clinical trial. There are very few slots available. The trial will not even start until sometime in October.

So our next plan of action is to set up a time to go to Bethesda over the next month and to return to Mass General in a month, to be considered for the clinical trial. Clearly, the MGH trial is the preferred option, but if he doesn't qualify, then we have a backup plan. There is good reason to be hopeful that one of these options will work.

The best news of the day was that the doctor would put John at the top of the list of potential clinical study participants if he can medically qualify. As usual, John's attitude is very positive and he says he will do what he needs to do to rid his body of this disease.

John is really enjoying the challenge of his new position as president of Cardinal Spellman High School. He feels well, he is not taking any pain medication, and his energy level is high. The other really good news was that the doctor approved our planned trip to Greece at the end of September.

The worst news that we could have received today would be that there were no more options. We are extremely grateful and we remain highly optimistic that we are being given options to beat the odds. This is possible through the medical team who are working with us and your continued support and prayers. You have no idea how much this has meant to us as a family. The sounds of hope were heard again today and we continue to treasure each day.

Love,
Margaret

John always had dreamed of some day giving service back, in some capacity, to his high school. The school's staff and the school community had been very good to him during a very difficult time in his life. In 2007, he had been appointed to the school's board of trustees. At the time he thought this would be his contribution of giving back. He was humbled when the Chairman of the Board asked him in 2008 if he would consider becoming the first lay president of the school. John had great faith and optimism that everything can have a purpose that happens in life. He thought it was fortuitous that he was being given this new opportunity to serve Spellman. (We had to ask ourselves if it was just a coincidence that he had this meeting with the Chairman of the Board earlier on the same day that John found out that he had cancer or was this some part of a greater plan?)

When John accepted the position at Spellman, he had not yet been diagnosed with cancer. After the diagnosis, he did not want the board to feel obligated to honor their agreement with him to serve as president since as he put it, "I am damaged goods. I can simply retire from public education and you can find someone else." The board told John he could work as much or as little as he wanted. He had no vacation or sick time because they knew he would do the best job he possibly could for them. John agreed to a three-year contract, not certain that he would be able to complete an entire year due to his health.

Although he was working full-time, he wanted to fit in as much travel as we possibly could. We were on an "accelerated" retirement plan. John had promised me a trip to Greece for our honeymoon, but when we got married 37 years before, we did not have the finances to go to Greece. In place of the promised trip, right after we were married we went to see the musical *Grease* in Boston. That was as close as I ever thought I would get to Greece in my lifetime. We always laughed about this.

My sister, Kathy, and I had had a double wedding. Sometimes we would share our anniversary celebrations together and sometimes separately. She had always wanted to go to Santorini when she retired. Her husband, Don, already retired, had been diagnosed with multiple myeloma, a cancer of the plasma cells, about seven months before John's diagnosis. As it happened, Kathy retired as an elementary school teacher the same year that John retired from public education. So together we planned the trip to Greece. We visited Athens to see the site of the first Olympics, the Acropolis and Delphi outside of Athens. We then went on a cruise stopping at Crete, Rhodes, Mykonos, and finally a stop in Ephesus. We ended the cruise by staying a few extra days on Santorini. The trip was evidence that dreams come true—even when both families were living under the cloud of cancer.

9

Clinical Trial MDX-1106

Throughout the centuries there were men
who took first steps down new roads armed
with nothing but their own vision.
—**Ayn Rand**

When we returned from our trip to Greece, we met with our oncologist, Dr. Lawrence, who told us that John did not qualify for the targeted cell therapy treatment. Our hearts sank. We thought our only other viable option was the course of treatment offered at the National Cancer Institute in Bethesda. To say we were disappointed would be an understatement.

Looking at us both with a cautious smile, the doctor said, "But we have a brand new option that was not available until two days ago. It is a promising new immunotherapy clinical trial, MDX-1106, offered by Bristol Myers Squibb, and John is a strong candidate."

There were only three slots available at Mass General for this clinical trial. John did qualify and got the last open slot. A brand new fantastic chapter in our cancer journey began!

—m—

October 7, 2009

Dear Family and Friends:

Yesterday afternoon we had a long consultation with John's oncologist. By the end of the visit, John had consented to participate in a brand new Phase II Clinical Study that is designed to help protect the body against foreign matter, such as bacteria and viruses. MDX-1106 is classified as an immunotherapy that boosts the immune system to recognize the cancer as foreign cells. The goal is to shrink the tumors and possibly eliminate them.

This study only became available on October 2 and John was the last participant allowed into the study. As they say at Cardinal Spellman High School, "God is good ... all the time." The doctor feels that this is an even better option than what he had proposed in August because John's cancer responded to the first Interleukin-2 treatment series, which is also an immunotherapy treatment. What the doctor is looking for is a sustained, continuous response.

The treatment involves an eight-week cycle of intravenous treatments every two weeks at Mass General. At the end of each eight-week cycle, John will have to undergo scans to see the effectiveness of the treatment. If the therapy appears to be working, he could stay on the treatment for up to three years. There are no known side effects, so John will be able to continue working. The doctor is really excited about being able to offer this option to us. And at the rate that the research is evolving right now, who knows what might be available three years from now?

John has not received any treatments since late July and we have enjoyed the break from the hospital and treatments. Although we don't look forward to the regimen of treatments, we knew that we needed to get into some type of program that would stop the growth of his cancer. We feel both very excited and blessed with the hope that this new treatment program offers.

During our break from treatments, we enjoyed our annual trip to Vermont, an overnight stay at our favorite bed and breakfast in Vermont and then a visit with old friends in New Hampshire.

And just last Sunday we returned from a trip to Greece that John had promised almost 37 years ago.

We are so blessed that we have been able to spend time with our family and friends and that John has been able to continue to work, to travel, and to continue to enjoy life to its fullest.

Thank you all for your continued support and prayers as we undergo this next step in our journey with cancer. Today we are filled with hope for continued blessings on our lives.

Love,

Margaret and John

As anyone who has ever undergone cancer treatments knows, the side effects from the chemotherapy or immunotherapy medications can be more physically annoying or emotionally draining than the disease itself. To ease access for blood draws and infusions, a port had been surgically implanted in John's chest. The port had been in place for almost a year. John had developed a rather large, very itchy, red rash that circled the area of the implanted port. He laughed it off and told several nurses that Target should use him in their advertisements.

John was not running a temperature and the skin was not warm to the touch, both indications of an infection. Several people had looked at it and could not determine the cause. Finally, a nurse who worked in the X-ray department observed that the circle was in the exact area where the skin around the port was sterilized with chlorhexidine gluconate before inserting the needle. She told John that he should tell everyone who accessed his port to use the old-fashioned method of sterilizing the skin with alcohol and iodopovidone. These applications were not always readily available throughout the hospital because chlorhexidine gluconate is so commonly used. To eliminate the problem, she gave me a supply to carry around so that I could provide it if needed. Sure enough after just a short time, the irritation, redness, and most importantly the itchy rash around his port was eliminated. Sometimes it is a simple solution together with the powers of a very observant caregiver that can eliminate a nagging problem. We credited this X-ray nurse as another one of John's angels.

—m—

December 8, 2009
Holiday Greetings to All:

There are highs and lows to all patients and their families who live with a chronic disease. John and I feel that among the most difficult are the days waiting for test results. John finished his first eight-week cycle of treatments on November 24, two days before Thanksgiving. On December 4, last Friday, John underwent a brain scan and CT scans of his chest and abdomen to determine whether or not he was responding to the new clinical trial drug, MDX-1106.

We were forewarned that this drug takes some time to work and not to expect too much from the early treatments. After a long four days, we finally found out today that his condition is stable. This means the doctors cannot see any new cancer sites and the tumors that he has have not grown significantly, and there actually has been some shrinkage.

These are definitely the best test results that we have received since last March when John finished his first series of Interleukin-2 treatments. We are certainly not out of the woods, but we are moving in a positive direction. These results ensured that today he was able to start his second series of four treatments that will take place over the next eight weeks. At the end of eight weeks, he will again have scans. It also means that we now have an eight-week reprieve that fortunately coincides with the holidays.

John has had a few side effects from the treatment, but he has been able to work every day. He looks well and feels the best he has felt in more than a year and a half. Just a few months ago, John would capitalize on the days or parts of days that he felt well, not knowing what the next day would bring. Well, I can attest to the fact that his good days are definitely occurring at a higher frequency level. Once again, I have to tell him to slow down so that I can keep up.

John's favorite season of the year is Christmas. This year, like last year, we feel so blessed and that we have so much to be grateful for. This has truly been the best year and the

most difficult year of our lives. We have great
faith in the doctors, nurses, and staff at Mass
General. They have treated us professionally
and personally as very special people. They
understand that we want to spend quality time
with our family and friends and they have made
every accommodation to ensure that this happens.

As much faith as we have in the medical
staff, we know that we have been blessed with a
phenomenal support network of family, friends,
and colleagues that will continue to help us
through this challenge. It is the season for the
renewal of hope, and we have every reason to
believe that we are being given what we need to
look forward to a healthier new year. We have good
reason to feel joy and we hope that you and your
families have found good reasons to be happy too.

May the peace, hope, and joy of the season be
yours,

Margaret and John

John's infusions lasted so long, and at times he became so
fatigued, he would ask to be assigned to a bed in a private
room rather than to a reclining chair in the open space.
The view from the reclining chairs of the Charles River was
incomparable, but he preferred the privacy of the room and
comfort of a bed. Besides, he was often working so it was
much quieter.

For most of the time that John was treated in the infusion center, his primary nurse was Danielle. She was an
outstandingly competent and caring professional who took
great pride in building a relationship with her patients. Each
visit, Danielle would walk into the room and give each of us

a big hug. She would then say, "How are you doing today? Have you had any symptoms or side effects that we need to talk about?" John typically would answer with a question. "I am doing fine, how are you and your babies doing? What did you do over the weekend?" She would then laugh and say, "Not so fast, mister, how are you really doing?" The two would banter back and forth, each eventually getting their questions answered.

There was one time when Danielle returned to John's room from visiting another patient and she appeared distracted. She said something that I have never forgotten. "While living with cancer, what you hope for changes." Over time, I gained a better understanding of what she meant by this statement. Initially everyone hopes for a cure or at least stabilization of the disease. As time goes along, you hope that you can continue to live productively while you have cancer. In the end, you hope that the patient does not have to suffer long from the disease or its side effects.

CHAPTER

10

Prolonged Honeymoon

The true secret of happiness lies in taking a
genuine interest in all the detail of daily life.
—William Morris

February 2, 2010

Dear Family and Friends:

When John's oncologist walked into his room today to report John's latest scan results, he had two thumbs way up. We hoped the news would be good but we weren't prepared for how good. John has had no new growth and an 11 percent reduction in all of his cancer sites. The doctor feels the radiology report of 11 percent is even conservative. This very professional, intelligent, compassionate physician walked right over to John's bedside and gave him a big hug, and then turned to me and did the same.

The doctor said this is an excellent response to just eight treatments over 16 weeks. John still has had minimal side effects and has been working full-time. He is off medications related to the cancer and has not been suffering the severe back pain that had occurred intermittently. In short, the news is really, really promising. He can continue on this treatment for as long as it works for him and the doctor feels strongly that the cancer sites will continue to diminish in size and may even be eliminated. We can only hope.... Whatever happens, we feel we have a course of medical treatment that may finally sustain control of John's cancer.

We feel so very blessed to have had such a positive response; but again, your kind thoughts and prayers have kept us afloat over the long waits in between results. Everyone was so positive and excited for us today at the hospital; there were lots of hugs going around the room. We just wish we could give each of you a hug from us for staying by us throughout this challenge.

Last year, on this very day, John was admitted to the hospital for his first Interleukin-2 treatment. As John was recovering from this very difficult treatment, he said he wanted to make plans for the whole family: a combined visit to Walt Disney World and a Disney Cruise. He said he needed to have something to look forward to. And he wanted it to be a long-term goal. We honestly didn't know when we made the plans during the Interleukin treatments in the summer of 2009, if John would be able to go. Well, in just nine days we are going to realize this dream of going to Disney with our children and grandchildren to celebrate dreams and hopes ... where John likes to do it best.

Each day is precious and we thank each of you

for being there to support us along the way.
A big hug to each of you!
Margaret and John

—〜〜〜—

John had the philosophy that if he worked hard, he wanted to play hard, and for him this meant traveling together as a couple or as a family. He believed in living in the moment and having good memories for the future. John's father had died in a tragic house fire when John was eight years old. This experience obviously had a profound impact on him. He never wanted to put off doing things with our own kids or with me because he believed that you just never knew what the future might bring.

Since John's diagnosis, we honestly never knew when we made travel plans if we would be able to follow through with them. Throughout his cancer journey, we felt that it was better to have the trips to look forward to than to disappoint ourselves by not making any travel plans at all. In retrospect, I know we both knew that our opportunities for time together would be limited so we would make the most of every day we had.

As part of a trip to Disney, John wanted to hire a professional photographer to take a family photo. We bought blue shirts for everyone and each brought a pair of tan colored pants. (Our four-year-old granddaughter insisted on wearing a blue dress!) Although it was taking some time away from our visits to the parks, everyone cooperated. This family photo holds very special memories for each of us and now hangs in an honored place in each of our homes. We also took advantage of this opportunity to have a photo taken of just the two of us.

We all enjoyed our stay at Disney World, but we were really looking forward to the experience of a cruise together. The irony was when we were checking into the Disney Cruise, the guest relations representative asked, "Are you celebrating any special occasion like a birthday or anniversary?" Without missing a beat, John responded, "I am celebrating life!" The woman gave him a big smile and handed him a badge that said "Celebrating Life." She whispered, "I was meant to check you in today so that we can celebrate together. It is my first day back to work since I received my successful cancer treatments." John proudly wore his badge throughout our cruise.

Naturally we felt very fortunate and excited as family to be taking this trip together. However, we often found that any day could feel special when someone offered an unexpected smile or kind remark. If you keep your eyes and ears open, even small parts of days can feel like a gift when you are living with a cancer diagnosis.

—⚒—

April 6, 2010

Dear Family and Friends:

Again today, John's oncologist walked into the room with two thumbs way up. He was so excited to report to us that the scans taken on Good Friday showed that John has had no new growth and a 30 percent reduction in all of his cancer sites. The 30 percent number is a measurement of the diameter of the sites, so the doctor explained that the actual cubic measure or volume of reduction is greater than 30 percent. The doctor walked over to John's bedside and said, "I hope you are a hugger." Hugs were shared around the room.

The doctor was truly ecstatic with these results. He said it was now official: John can be classified as a "responder" to this treatment.

The doctor said that as long as John is not suffering any major side effects, which he is not, he can continue on this treatment as a maintenance program. He was so excited about the results he showed us the actual CAT scans on a computer so that we could get a visual of John's progress.

Later, the staff told us that Dr. Lawrence had blasted e-mails to all of John's caregivers to share this great news. Everyone commented on just how happy the doctor was when they met him throughout the morning. It is so great to have a doctor who knows his field of medicine so well, who is on the cutting edge of medical treatments, and who can also be so compassionate with his patients. We are so blessed!

We are not sure whether John will be allowed to stay on this medication when the official clinical trial period ends. Dr. Lawrence said that the MGH Cancer Center would appeal to the drug company to ensure that John could continue treatments as long as there are no long-term problems with the treatment.

It goes without saying that we feel that extra blessings of the Easter season have been showered upon us. We feel so very fortunate to have had the opportunity to participate in this clinical trial. However, we never take for granted the kind thoughts and prayers that each of you have shared with us. We truly value your love, friendship, and support.

Today was the beginning of a new cycle of treatments. We have now been able to sustain this treatment plan for six months. Needless to say, with results like this, John is planning several more trips ... but we have to plan around the treatment schedule. How lucky are we that we can make plans not only a few weeks out, but we are now talking about what we would like to do during the summer of 2011? Of course, spring and summer trips for 2010 are already planned.

Each day is precious; each season is to be celebrated. We wish you all the joy of good news and we thank each of you for being there to support us along the way.

Oh, Happy Spring!!!!

Margaret and John

I always did the driving to and from the hospital appointments so that John was free to work as needed. He had been following the introduction of the new Apple product: the first version of the iPad. On our way home from the hospital on April 6, he said, "Would you stop at the Apple Store at the Plaza so that I can see these new iPads for myself?" Of course I agreed and John and I were introduced to this new electronic device.

He was sold on the idea before he ever crossed the store's threshold because he had been using an iPhone for some time now. He was so excited with his medical news that he wanted to celebrate by investing in what he thought would be cutting-edge technology for students in his school going forward.

John's enthusiasm was always contagious. Over time, I got so engaged with the iPad, I finally broke down and bought an iPhone and much later a MacBook Pro laptop. This allowed me to integrate all of my electronic devices. Of course, if John ran into a problem, he could ask someone in the school's technology department to figure it out. I was left more to my own devices to solve a problem.

In the spring of 2010, John had another home improvement project in mind. He wanted to replace the windows in the original part of our house. Of course this was a major home renovation that I did not think we had to be dealing with at the time. John insisted that when it came time for us to eventually sell the house this would be an attractive feature. Once more, he was trying to prepare the house for me to be able to stay in it if I chose to when he was gone.

—ᴫ—

June 1, 2010

Dear Family and Friends:

Today, John received great results from his most recent scans. John's oncologist again walked into the room with a big smile on his face. He said he had not received the official measurements yet from the clinical study's radiologist, but visually all cancer sites appeared either stable or shrinking. The doctor said he feels that John will be able to continue on this treatment as a maintenance plan, as long as we are willing to go to the hospital every two weeks. Let's just say we are more than happy to fit this into our schedule!

The doctor will go to Chicago this weekend to the national conference on all types of cancer. MDX-1106, the name of the treatment John is on, will be reported out in a session. The doctor said that in the field of melanoma, the results that John is achieving are truly exciting and promising and what he works for every day!

Speaking of success stories, the doctor asked if we would be interested in meeting his other patient who is responding so well to this treatment. We enthusiastically agreed and we have plans to meet her and her husband for dinner in a couple of weeks. We are all very excited that we were able to arrange this meeting.

Today was the start of the fifth cycle of treatments. So we are now cleared to go on our next adventure to the national parks. We are planning to go to the Grand Tetons, Yellowstone, and Mount Rushmore at the end of June. This has been on the list for a while and now we can fulfill our plan to go.

Our oncologist, Dr. Lawrence, personally shares all of our joys and sorrows in this journey. As do all of you. We never take for granted the kind thoughts and prayers that each of you have shared with us. We are so blessed!

Each day is precious ... we have so much to celebrate. Thank you for sharing our journey with us. Have a wonderful summer!

Love,

Margaret and John

July 27, 2010

Dear Family and Friends:

John had scans on Friday and today we learned that the results continue to be good. His tumors continue to decrease in size, especially the one on his spine that was the source of his pain. It is great to get these good results confirmed with scans, but we know that he has been feeling better than he has for two years. He is taking absolutely no pain medication, and his tolerance for physical activity has improved.

Although we anticipate good news, we never

feel relief until we hear it from the doctor. We also never take it for granted that we have had an amazing opportunity to have access to this clinical trial, nor do we take for granted the hope and support that you continue to provide to us. Each day brings a new face of hope into our lives through a kind deed, a word of support, or a genuine demonstration of empathy for what we have been going through. We truly believe that this is a sign that God has heard all of our prayers.

We had a wonderful trip to Yellowstone, the Grand Tetons, and Mount Rushmore, including a raft ride on the Snake River and a trail ride on horses at a dude ranch. We are so grateful for the opportunities that we have had to travel together, especially in the past two years!

So, life is good for us and we hope for you as well. Enjoy the rest of the summer!

Love,

Margaret and John

September 21, 2010

Dear Family and Friends:

Dr. Lawrence walked into the room with both thumbs up ... again! Since April, we only have been told that the scans continue to show that the tumors are shrinking. Today, Dr. Lawrence told us with a big smile that the tumors have shrunk a total of 38.5 percent in diameter, which means that the total volume has shrunk even more.

No matter how many times we have gotten positive results from this clinical trial, the outcome is only good for eight weeks ... until the next set of scans. John explained to the doctor that he keeps waiting for "the shoe to drop." The doctor's response was that "the shoes are dancing today!"

As happy as we are with these results, the doctor told us that the drug company would not extend this clinical trial to any additional patients. The doctor reassured us that John will be able to carry on with his treatments, but the company has made the business decision to concentrate its resources on the manufacturing, marketing, and distribution of a related drug, Ipilimumab. In the medical field, the drug is commonly referred to simply as "Ipi" and it is very close to receiving FDA approval.

We never take for granted how lucky we have been to have the opportunity to participate in this clinical trial. We were truly saddened to hear this news today that others will not be given the same chance. It is amazing how a business decision in clinical research can affect the life and potential death of someone you love.

John has offered to write a letter to the drug company to give a face to the success of the MDX-1106 treatment. The doctor enthusiastically supported John's offer for help because John's success is indicative of how others with melanoma could potentially be treated. Dr. Lawrence feels that the future treatments of cancer will be multifaceted rather than isolated. Limiting the research dollars for this drug eliminates one potentially powerful opportunity for treatment and hope for many others.

As a parent, you always hope that each of your children will find happiness in their lives ... and perhaps someone to share it with. We now believe that both John and I will have one more prayer answered. Next summer, John will be able to walk our youngest child, Julie, down the aisle to start her life with a very special guy named Greg. We hope that they will find the same happiness in marriage that we continue to have.

We have many reasons for the shoes to continue to dance! Thank you all for sharing our joy in this dance of our lives.

Love,

Margaret and John

—⟋⟍—

Christmas 2010

Holiday greetings!

The holiday season returns this year with more hope and joy than we could possibly imagine! Each day of the past year has been a blessing and we look forward to the New Year with an even greater sense of optimism.

John and two other patients at Mass General are making medical history with their response to a clinical trial for the treatment of melanoma. In mid-November we received outstanding results from John's scans. The tumors have shrunk a total of 47 percent in diameter ... almost 10 percent shrinkage from just eight weeks ago. The doctor believes that now that John's immunological system has been "triggered," the tumors will continue to shrink. He even thinks that at this time next year, he may not even need regular treatments, just regular follow-ups. It is truly a miracle!

John has now been on this trial for 14 months. As we have said for the past two and a half years, the medicine is working but the thoughts and prayers that we have received have been our true sense of support as we live with cancer.

After John retired from public education in the summer of 2009, he started working for his alma mater, Cardinal Spellman High School, as president. He agreed to take the position because he was looking to slow down his pace, but John never keeps things simple. Along with enhancing the technology, curriculum, professional development, and the financial accountability, he has been working very hard on a three-phase building project. His goal now is to see the building projects through. As for me I continue to enjoy volunteering throughout the year for My Brother's Keeper, an organization that brings the hope and love of Jesus to people in need through the delivery of food and furniture.

Although John needs treatments every two weeks, we value the time we get to spend together with family and friends. We find it is good to have both short- and long-term plans as we live with this chronic disease. In February, we celebrated life with all of our children and grandchildren on a trip to Disney World and on the Disney Cruise Line ... something we had planned when John was seriously ill over a year ago.

In April, we took a trip to Hawaii, which was where we first realized, two and a half years ago, that something was physically wrong with John. We never thought we would have a return trip! At the end of June, we went on the trip of a lifetime to the Grand Tetons, Yellowstone, and Mount Rushmore. You cannot help but stand in awe at the wonders of nature and the talents of man.

Finally in early December we met our son, Chris, and his family at Universal Studios in Orlando to experience the new "Harry Potter" ride and then a holiday visit to Disney. John wanted to see the parks during the holiday season. (Some things have no element of surprise.) We thoroughly enjoyed sharing this experience through the eyes of a two-year-old! Oh, the joys of grandchildren.

Last year at this time we were hoping that we could find a treatment plan that would allow us to spend more time together. This year we are thanking God, our medical doctors and nurses, and our family and friends that we have been given reason to have new hope that we will be able to continue to live with this disease for many years to come.

May this year bring all of you the hope that we have been blessed with and the peace in knowing that "we don't always get what we want, but we do get what we need."

Peace and joy,
Margaret and John

11

Life Is Good

You gain strength, courage, and confidence by every experience in which you really stop to look fear in the face. You are able to say to yourself, "I lived through this horror. I can take the next thing that comes along."
—**Eleanor Roosevelt**

March 8, 2011

Dear Family and Friends:

The news continues to be good. We were told today there are no new cancer sites and the tumors have shrunk by about 50 percent. John looks and feels healthy and his energy level is high! Dr. Lawrence, who was featured on a Channel 5 news segment for another cancer protocol, remains very excited about John's sustained response in this program.

Thank you to all for your continued support throughout this journey.

We saw three robins in the backyard last week. So we know by the bird's calendar we can begin our celebration of spring!

Love,

Margaret and John

May 3, 2011

Dear Family and Friends:

The beat goes on and the rhythm is good! Again the scans show stable results and no new cancer sites. John looks and feels healthy and his energy level is great. He is helping with some household chores that he wasn't able to do last year. (That's good for me ... not so much for him!)

After two years in this clinical trial, John's participation is scheduled to end in October. We were starting to get anxious about what the next steps would be. The best news we got today is that Dr. Lawrence will keep John on this treatment plan as long as he continues to get favorable results. Dr. Lawrence shared with us again just how excited he is about John's continued response to the treatment, especially considering the advanced stage of disease John was dealing with just 19 months ago.

When we told Dr. Lawrence that we are looking forward to the birth of a new grandchild and the wedding of our youngest daughter this summer, he said, "That's what this work is all about." It is so great to work with a doctor who appreciates the milestones that we have all been able to achieve together.

In fact, MGH has just been approved to add four more patients to an expanded clinical trial. Dr.

Lawrence asked John if he would be willing to talk to a few of the potential candidates. Of course he said, "Yes."

Although we hope to keep this rhythm going for a long, long time, we know that each day is a gift.

Thank you to all for your continued support throughout this journey.

Love,

Margaret and John

June 27, 2011

Dear Family and Friends:

When John started this clinical trial in October 2009, we felt so blessed to be among the participants of a clinical trial that offered two years of treatment and a third year of follow-up. Nothing up to that point sounded so promising. This month we realized that the trial was designed for 12 cycles of eight weeks. Today we started our 12th cycle, which means that John will stop treatments in August and then receive monthly follow-ups and scans every three months.

Our doctor did appeal to the drug company to allow John to continue receiving treatments because he has done so well. Although the drug is still being manufactured, and they have added a few more people to a new trial, the manufacturer refused. As we have been told in the past, the drug triggers the immune system and after this long series of treatments, it is expected to continue to shrink the tumors, keep them stable and prevent others from growing. This is what the drug company is trying to evaluate at this point.

As with everything related to this disease, it is the unknown that is so unsettling. When you establish a series of treatments and see a network of health-care workers on a regular basis, it becomes part of your normal and comfortable routine.

The doctor has reassured us that he will continue to follow John very closely. If the tumors start to grow, the doctor will again appeal to the drug company to reinstitute a treatment therapy plan. We have every confidence that he will follow through.

We feel so blessed that John has done so well. We have continued to enjoy good health and a very high quality of life for the past two years. We have celebrated family birthdays and enjoyed gatherings with family and friends. This past week we were blessed with our fourth grandchild. And this summer, we are looking forward to seeing our youngest daughter married … all milestones we had hoped to achieve together in good health.

So there is much to celebrate and we do … every day! Thank you for your continued prayers and support during this journey.

May you all have a wonderful summer and enjoy each day as a gift!

Love,

Margaret and John

August 23, 2011

Dear Family and Friends:

As we age, many people try to overlook their birthdays. But as a family living with cancer, we celebrate every single one: our grandchildren's, our children's and their spouses, and our own. This weekend we celebrated John's birthday ... all weekend long! And the celebration continued today with very good results from the scans taken on Friday. There are no new cancer sites and the three that are there are either stable or reduced in size.

The treatments have ended but the follow-up for the clinical trial continues. The best part of the follow-up phase is that we get to see some of the oncology team that we had not seen while John was on the infusion floor. It was like visiting with old friends.

The plan now is for us to go in monthly to Mass General for routine work and then every eight weeks John will receive another set of scans. The following week we will get the results from the doctor and John will undergo a physical and more blood work. So now we have to sit tight and just see how things go.

During all of this, John has never doubted his faith, his trust in his doctor and medical team, his appreciation of the support network that he has, and his positive attitude towards life. Last week, he even led a day-long student leadership workshop. Even one year ago, as good as he felt, he would not have had the stamina to do it.

We have had a summer of celebrations; the birth of our fourth grandchild and our daughter's wedding. Several years ago, John and our daughter, Julie, heard the song, "Somewhere Over the Rainbow," by Iz, and promised each other that they would dance to that song someday at her wedding. Witnessed by family and friends, John and Julie got to keep their promise to each other. Our entire family celebrated this happy milestone.

Although we have experienced ups and downs in this journey, we never lose sight of how blessed we have been in the big picture of life.

So again, there is much to celebrate and we do ... every day! Thank you for your continued prayers and support during this journey.

Love,

Margaret and John

12

Readmittance into the Clinical Trial

The difficult we do immediately,
the impossible takes a little longer.
—U.S. Army slogan during World War II

October 18, 2011
   Dear Family and Friends:
We are living a new chapter in our cancer journey. John is not receiving treatments and the doctor is following up with scans, blood work, and a physical every eight weeks. Today we received the first results since he has been out of treatments. As much as we had hoped that the sites would continue to shrink in size, we were happy that he remains stable and there are no new sites.
   It was great to get the results directly from our doctor and to get his reassurance that should John's sites increase significantly in size, he

will re-petition the drug company to put John back on the clinical trial treatment plan. The doctor expressed frustration that the drug company has restricted the number of melanoma patients on this clinical trial for MDX-1106 because they have made the decision to invest the research dollars into other cancers that have no other proven alternatives. (This spring, the FDA approved Ipilimumab, now sold as Yervoy, for the treatment of melanoma.) Needless to say, the approved drug would be available to John, should he need it, but we would prefer that he could get the clinical trial drug since he has done so well with it.

John continues to feel great and looks wonderful. His energy level is extraordinarily high. We never take for granted that John has regained his ability to climb long flights of stairs and to just stand for hours at a time. There were times when he could not do these routine tasks.

Just one month ago, we celebrated our grandson Max's third birthday with him. It truly was a celebration of his life and ours since the day he was born was the day we found out that John's cancer had spread. We are beating the odds and our lives have been blessed with so many reasons to celebrate.

We have so much to be grateful for again this Thanksgiving season. Each day is a blessing and we thank you all for your continued prayers and support.

Love,

Margaret and John

—〰—

Thanksgiving Letter to Cardinal Spellman Faculty 2011

My wife is a voracious reader. I am ashamed that I do not even come near the amount of reading that she does or the quality of the literature she reads. Maybe someday! Recently she finished a book about Hungarian Jews struggling in labor camps during World War II titled "The Invisible Bridge" by Julie Orringer. The book was very sad but also very moving. At the end of the book was a poem by Wislawa Szymborska, a Polish author who received The Nobel Prize in Literature 1996 for "poetry that with ironic precision allows the historical and biological context to come to light in fragments of human reality." Margaret completed the book in the middle of the night and first thing the next morning she said, "You've got to read this poem."

The poem is a reflection on unexplainable things that happen in our lives and to those whom we love. Last Friday, I visited a woman with whom I used to teach who had a horrible accident in July. She was walking across the street in New Hampshire on the first day of her vacation. Somehow, a truck struck her. Somehow, she moved quickly enough to feel the tire against her face but ... somehow she moved just enough to not be crushed. Somehow she mangled her leg. Somehow she was hospitalized and faced many operations and a great deal of physical therapy. And ... somehow she still has great faith and is thankful to still be alive. She has no idea how or why she survived. She is working on finding that answer.

There is a very thin line between "luck" and "faith." One of the greatest challenges that face any of us is the reality that "bad things happen to good people," and that no one, including Jesus Christ, ever said, "life would be fair." We just don't know the "whys." It is learning to accept that reality that truly makes us "wise."

At Spellman this year, we have much for which to be thankful. Unlike many Catholic schools that face closing or consolidation, we are moving forward and building a strong future for our school. We have a great faculty and staff that work very hard for every student in the school. We can be very proud of the faith community and the service that our students do. Our enrollment is always a scary challenge but, somehow, we are optimistic that our school will survive.

The poem is about survival. Isn't that what all life is about ... survival? Any time I meet a new teacher or work with someone in a new role, I always say, "Your only goal is survival." No matter what challenges are thrown in front of us, the important thing is to face them, overcome them, and then move on to the next phase of our lives. Those challenges can be with health, finances, personal relations, faith, or almost anything. It is having the personal resources, along with faith and determination, that help us survive. The next step after to survive is to flourish. That is my dream for Spellman!

This year, I personally have much to be thankful for. However, I never take any good that happens or bad that threatens for granted. I know that a combination of both good and bad is inevitable. I do know, however, it is through faith, hard work, a bit of luck, and support from family and friends that we all survive. It is through

faith in God and forbearance that we learn how to
flourish and to work to make our dreams come true:
for us, for those whom we love, and for our school.

This Thanksgiving and throughout the year,
I truly appreciate all that you do for Spellman's
students. I am thankful that I have had the
opportunity to be both a part of Spellman's
survival and that I have the challenge, along with
all of you, to help Spellman flourish in the future.
This January I will resolve to read more, especially
works of quality. However, this Thanksgiving I
thank God for my wonderful wife who shares her
reading with me and for the opportunity to reflect
on why all of us have so much to be thankful for.

Happy Thanksgiving to you and your family!
John

———ɯɯ———

December 13, 2011

Dear Family and Friends:

We received really encouraging news today that
although John has been off treatment for 16 weeks,
his melanoma sites continue to remain stable. The
doctor, with a big smile on his face, shrugged his
head and said we have been "at this" for quite a
long time! In fact, it has now been three and a
half years since we got the grim news that John's
cancer had spread. In the treatment of metastatic
melanoma, these are indeed miraculous results.

The doctor will continue to monitor John's
cancer very closely. Our next goal would be for the
cancer sites to stabilize to the point where the
doctor would feel that he could spread out the time
between scans. However, should the cancer sites

grow we do have a couple of options. John and I agree that any options are good. The doctor reassured us we may continue to plan for the future. With his unique perspective on life he told us that we can "go out and buy green bananas."

More research continues to be done at Mass General in the treatment of melanoma. Our doctor informed us that there are three more clinical trials that will be introduced in the near future. He is still lobbying with the drug company to expand the number of patients with melanoma to use the treatment that was so successful for John and now five other patients.

A cancer diagnosis changes your life forever. Each day is a gift and every opportunity to celebrate a birthday or holiday is a blessing. We look forward to Christmas this year, with renewed hope and excitement about the year ahead.

We have all been "at this" for a long time and you have never wavered in your support and prayers. May you feel as blessed as we do to celebrate this holiday season together with family and friends. And may you all look forward to a year of hope and many more opportunities to "buy green bananas."

Love,

Margaret and John

—⟲⟲—

Christmas 2011

Holiday greetings! We hope that you and your families can take the time to reflect on all the true joy of the season and the chance for renewal that the New Year brings.

Considering John's original prognosis of

six months to a year was given more than three years ago, we have realized and cherished more dreams together than we ever thought possible. At this time last year, we hoped that John might not need regular treatments, just regular checkups. Since August, he has not received treatments. His cancer has not been eradicated but it is clinically stable. We understand that this is not a permanent condition, so we take advantage of every opportunity we can to visit with family, reconnect with friends, and to travel.

After years of witnessing my mother's failing health, she finally had her wish granted and was called home to God. Four days before her death, my niece gave birth to her first child and wanted her daughter's name to reflect the strong female role models she has had in her life. Her daughter's name is Anna, after my mother. Even in her confused state of health and spirit, Anna's birth brought a smile to Mom's face and tears to her eyes.

Reunions with old friends and classmates have enriched our lives, that in other circumstances, we may have put off. We have also enjoyed two amazing trips this year, the first to the Canadian Rockies and the second to the Amalfi Coast. Certainly different, but both had majestically unique landscapes and memorable and charming people.

The McEwan family has been blessed this year with the birth of our fourth grandchild, Trenton Christopher, born to Chris and Liz. His big brother, Max, immediately dubbed him "Mr. Trenty." We look forward to the family visiting from Charlotte during Christmastime when we will celebrate Trent's christening.

At the end of July we celebrated our daughter Julie's wedding. Heather was her sister's matron of honor, and our grandchildren were also part of the wedding party. It truly was a celebration of a very happy milestone for our entire family. When we told John's oncologist, Dr. Lawrence, about this happy occasion he said, "It makes me very happy when my patients can reach these milestones. This is what my work is all about."

John started his third year of "retirement" as the head of Cardinal Spellman High School. John's 45th Class Reunion at his alma mater was held at Cardinal Spellman's new fitness center, a welcomed addition to the gymnasium built 54 years ago. The school has totally remodeled the science labs. Other changes have added more rigor to the curriculum, the provision of a Wi-Fi network throughout the entire school, and the introduction of iPads to all teachers this year. During the next school year, students will begin to replace textbooks with iPads, providing them with the resources for a 21st century education.

Although we have experienced ups and downs in this journey of life, John and I have not lost sight of how blessed we have been in the big picture. So again, there is much to celebrate this year and we do … every day! We continue to thank God for the opportunity to live with this disease and in doing so enjoy living life to its fullest.

May you all be so blessed!
Margaret and John

———※———

No one but John would have predicted the purchase of his personal iPad in April of 2010 would lead to the integration of iPads into the school's curriculum. John was always a visionary and thinking of ways to improve how students could become more active learners.

The Mac tablets, or iPads, had been invented not as a replacement for an iPhone or MacBook Pro Laptop, but as a user-friendlier portable device that was larger than a mobile phone but not as cumbersome as a computer. One person described the difference to me by saying a computer is like a refrigerator, but the tablet is like a lunch box. For schools, it allows students and teachers to have access to the Internet, to use e-mail, and—most importantly for a private school—to allow students to buy and download books at a much lower cost than traditional books. Students must buy their own books in most private schools and now the information would be up-to-date. John established a technology committee to evaluate the possibility of replacing some of the textbooks with iPads. After two years of study, the committee voted to go forward with the idea and present it to the board of trustees for approval. Cardinal Spellman High School was among the first schools to introduce the use of iPads in September of 2012. Teachers were issued an iPad in December of 2011 so that they would become familiar with them. They were also offered instruction on how to integrate the use of iPads for actively engaged learning opportunities in the classroom. Students rented the iPads from the school for a fee. This arrangement gave the school control over the accessibility of approved websites.

—⚅—

February 7, 2012
    Dear Family and Friends:
    We received the results of John's most recent scans today. The good news is that John has no new sites, and all but one site have decreased in

size by over 60 percent. However, he has one nodule on his lung that continues to increase in size. Because most of the sites are diminishing in size, John is not a candidate for the clinical trial treatment that has successfully interfered with the progression of the disease. In other words, because John's condition is stable, the doctor now recommends that the one growing lesion in his lung be surgically removed in the near future.

John will undergo a PET scan to confirm the exact size of the lesion and to check his entire body for any potential "hot spots" that cannot be picked up with MRIs or scans. Although he has had scans and MRIs every eight weeks, John hasn't undergone a PET scan since August of 2009.

John is scheduled to see the thoracic surgeon to discuss the results of the PET scan on February 22 and hopefully have the surgery early in March. It will be a video-assisted thorascopic surgery, which is minimally invasive. John will only be expected to stay one or two nights in the hospital, and recovery is expected to be fairly quick. The doctor said if John's job were physically chal-lenging, then he would have to take more time for recovery. We are all grateful that John's livelihood has not been dependent on his physical prowess.

Both John and I expected that at some point in time he would require surgery. We were both happy that the doctor suggested in December that this might be an option for a treatment plan. It allowed us both to mentally prepare for it. The doctor said that with the elimination of this site, there is a strong possibility that we might be able to look forward to years (yes, years) of no treatments.

Certainly, it is a great option and we again

consider ourselves among the very fortunate to have survived almost four years with Stage IV Melanoma. Dr. Lawrence reassures us that this is medical history in the making. In summary, the clinical trial has interrupted the progress of the disease and the surgery should remove the one lesion that continues to grow. It improves his odds for the long term.

So with continued prayers and support from all of you, we are hopeful that once again we can put another successful chapter in our journey of hope. In the meantime, we leave tomorrow for a trip to Disney with our son and his family. We are so blessed to be able to celebrate living with hope every day.

Love,
Margaret and John

—∭—

February 22, 2012
Dear Family and Friends:
Today was the day we expected to meet with the thoracic surgeon for a consult. Instead, we got a call to see the oncologist to discuss the PET scan that John was given a week ago.

John hasn't had a PET scan since August of 2009, so we were anxious to get these results prior to the planned surgery. The good news is that all of John's cancer sites are far below the baseline measurements taken before participating in the clinical trial two and a half years ago. In fact, two of the original sites are totally gone. Surgery would have been the best option if John's cancer had remained stable other than the one site that they planned to surgically remove from his lung. The PET scan showed three new sites that had not been picked up by the CT scans that John has received every eight weeks over the course of two and a half years.

So the treatment plan has changed and the oncologist has some new options available to us. He has petitioned the drug company to allow John to be put back on the experimental drug that has given him such fantastic results. However, he told us that John might not meet the qualifications of being in a "progressive disease" state. We will know their response in the next few days.

Although the clinical trial drug, MDX-1106, would be our first choice, John is a candidate for a drug that has been approved by FDA called Ipilimumab, commercially know as Yervoy. The goal with the alternative treatment plan would be to get John stabilized so that surgery might be an option again in one or two years.

It has been six months since John has received any kind of treatment and we have enjoyed the freedom, but knew that his condition would at some point require further treatment. We thought that it would be surgery, but that has changed with the more sophisticated scan results. Thank God for them. Together with the doctor we can make a more informed choice about the options available to us.

John and I continue to have faith that we can and will live with cancer as a chronic disease for years to come. Together with our children we sincerely thank you all for your continued support and prayers. Our hope is that each of you will be as blessed as we have been with family and friends who have been there for us.

Love,
Margaret and John

———m———

March 12, 2012

Dear Family and Friends:

After almost three weeks of anxious waiting, we met with John's oncologist today to find out what his new treatment plan will be. After much deliberation and evaluation, the doctor and his team have decided to take what he called a "strategic approach" to treating John's cancer. They have decided not to change anything at this point in time.

The good news is that John's cancer continues to respond to the clinical trial drug and overall his cancer sites have been markedly reduced. The doctor believes if there is not a cure for John's cancer, he can deal with it as a chronic condition for the foreseeable future.

All the cancer sites have been reduced by 42 percent from the baseline from two and a half years ago. The doctor feels that the clinical trial drug, MDX-1106, continues to work on all but one very small tumor, and he wants to observe the ongoing effects of this drug. The sites that were reported to us as "new" during the last visit actually had been there, but had not shown up as "hot spots" until the most recent PET scan was done. The fact that he didn't have any new sites was a great relief to us.

The doctor understands that it is difficult for cancer patients not to be in some kind of treatment program. However, the "strategic approach" is that he will observe John's condition for another six months to a year. He will continue to have CT scans and MRIs every eight weeks. From the results of these tests, the doctor will decide if surgery is the best option or if an alternative plan needs to be put into place.

These are the best results we could have hoped for. We can and will live with cancer as a chronic disease. John told the doctor during our visit that we thanked God for these good results and we thanked him as well. The doctor responded by saying, "Always thank God first." We do. And we thank each of you for your continued support. It truly means so much to us that we have so many praying on our behalf. We truly believe this has given us this gift of time.

Love,

Margaret and John

—⚏—

April 3, 2012

Dear Family and Friends:

As John and I were driving through the city streets today to get to Mass General, he said: "Wouldn't it be great if life were just right turns." Today we got the news that we are going to have to take a left turn to get to where we want to be.

When malignant tumors have grown and they respond to treatment, the disease state is then measured from the lowest reduction point. Overall, John had achieved outstanding results from the clinical trial drug, MDX-1106. John received the full dosage of the clinical trial drug and the plan was to monitor him for 12 months. During that time, the doctor was evaluating the growth and/

or reduction in size of all sites. John has not received any treatments for eight months.

Total measurements for all of John's cancer sites have gone down since he started the MDX-1106. However, a 20 percent growth of just one or more sites classifies the disease as "progressive." John's most recent scans show that although the one lesion on his lung is still much smaller than when he started, it has now reached the 20 percent growth marker. (This is the same site that had been considered for surgery just four weeks ago.) All other sites continue to either shrink or remain stable.

The doctor is again appealing to the drug company to approve the continuation of MDX-1106. John responded well to the drug and had no serious side effects. The doctor expects that a second round of treatment could be even more effective. If he can get their approval, John would have to pass some tests, and then get started with treatments in the next few weeks. The goal is to go back on treatment, achieve even better results, and strive for ongoing maintenance therapy.

Whatever happens, it is likely that John and I will be spending more time together. The time we spend together is precious, no matter what we are doing. So, we are happy to go back into a treatment plan that will bring us back into "more right turns" in this cancer journey.

With your continued support and prayers, we know that we can achieve this goal.

Love,

Margaret and John

April 6, 2012, Good Friday

Dear Family and Friends:

God must have been barraged with prayers because late this afternoon our prayers were answered.

The drug company has agreed to extend John's treatment using the clinical trial drug, MDX-1106. We don't have any details yet but we are going into MGH again next week for some tests and to get our new schedule. The doctor wants to get John back into treatment as soon as possible.

We feel so blessed that John will receive this treatment that has worked for him before. We can only hope that it will be even more effective with this round.

The following week we have a trip planned to the Outer Banks. We are so happy to have this opportunity to celebrate life with our children, grandchildren, and some extended family.

One of John's favorite quotes is: "The difficult we do immediately. The impossible takes a little longer." May marks the fourth anniversary of John's diagnosis. The journey has had its ups and downs but it certainly has been rewarding in more ways than we can count.

May you all enjoy a Blessed Easter!

Love,

Margaret and John

We had rented a very large house on the ocean and my sister and her extended family joined us to celebrate another family vacation that we had wanted to take for some time.

On the car ride down to the Outer Banks, we walked around Williamsburg, Virginia, had dinner in one of the taverns and stayed overnight. We started the next day at Busch Gardens in Williamsburg. My four-year-old granddaughter and I were waiting for the rest of our party to join us at Busch Gardens when I commented on her sundress. I said, "Keira, my mother loved bright colorful patterns, she would have loved your dress." (My mother had died six months before.) Keira did not miss a beat and responded by opening her arms wide and said, "But sadly, she died." She hesitated and then said, "But don't worry, Grammy, you will be with her soon!" These are the cherished moments that make every day activities spent with grandkids so special.

While we were staying at the house in the Outer Banks, we had a wonderful time building sandcastles on the beach, flying kites, and playing games together. Again, John wanted a family photo taken, but we knew we had a couple of grandkids that were often uncooperative when put in front of a camera.

We resorted to bribery! For the three-year-old, it was a promise of some immediate gratification. But the seven-year-old was a little more challenging. As we had been driving down to the Outer Banks, he had asked if we could stop in Washington, DC on the way. He had read a book about Abraham Lincoln and wanted a firsthand look at the Lincoln Memorial. John promised him that if he cooperated in taking the family photo then we would stop on our way home.

The day of the photo shoot was particularly windy on the beach. Our grandson, Zachary, was very well behaved during the entire photo shoot. The minute the photographer announced he was done, Zachary ran up to his grandfather and asked, "Have I been good enough to stop at the Lincoln Memorial on our way home?" Grandpa said, "Absolutely!"

What Grandpa had not taken into account was that parking restrictions had been imposed in and around the city since 9/11. They no longer allow cars to park close to many of the government buildings, the national museums, or memorials. John could not walk long distances. We drove around the block several times and saw other memorials, but we could not seem to get close to the Lincoln. Grandpa said, "Zach, I am sorry but we can only go around one more time and then we are going to have to postpone this visit until the next time you come here." No sooner had he said that than a van pulled out of a very convenient parking space. Once we parked, Zachary jumped out of the car and raced up the steps.

When John caught up to him, Zach was standing in awe and pinching his arm. John asked, "What are you doing, Zach?"

"I am pinching myself because I cannot believe I am really here."

John was bursting with pride and shed a little tear to think this meant so much to Zachary and that he was there to witness it.

The photos from this vacation are treasured memories of the wonderful days we spent with the people we love. We had photos taken of the whole family as well as individual family photos. Even little Hannah, who never met her grandfather, looks at this family picture displayed on the family room bookshelf and proudly says, "That's my grandpa. He died you know!"

The moral to this story is to do things together, and if you can, take photos. They do not have to be formal photos but they will capture a moment in time that can never be repeated.

—⚬⚬—

June 5, 2012
    Dear Family and Friends:
    Over this past weekend, Reuters released a

press statement nationally and internationally from the American Society of Clinical Oncology conference in Chicago reporting on the promising results from a drug, BMS-93665 (formerly known as MDX-1106). The Bristol-Meyers Squibb clinical trials have demonstrated that the drug has effectively shrunk tumors in patients with advanced stages of melanoma, kidney, and lung cancers. Our doctor said that you could hear and sense the excitement among the attendees about these results. Twenty-eight percent of the 94 melanoma patients had significant tumor shrinkage, and John is lucky to be among the success stories.

It is hard to believe John already has received four treatments since being back on the clinical trial. He had some initial fatigue when he started receiving treatments again, but after a couple of weeks he was back to his usual energy level, which to me is exhausting.

Today we received his first set of results from scans. We were prepared that with the reintroduction of the drug into John's system that the drug would trigger the growth of the sites. The doctor informed us today that that is exactly what has happened. There has been slight growth in all tumors. When John was first put on the drug it took six months for him to see positive results. So, if he follows the same course we should expect to see significant shrinkage by September.

Only 203 people throughout the country have participated in this clinical trial and of that number 94 have melanoma. Mass General is conducting three other clinical trials with drugs that remove the natural brake on immune system cells. According to the report, these drugs are not just shrinking the tumors, they are "training the immune system" to continue to attack cancer cells. It is truly exciting to be able to be a part of such groundbreaking results.

While John had a respite from treatments, we made plans to take a Baltic cruise that he has wanted to do now for five years. The doctor has worked out John's treatment schedule so that we will be able to go on this cruise during the summer.

We believe the medicine is a miracle but we also believe that the prayers from all of you have sustained us. Thank you for your part in our journey.

Love,

Margaret and John

The quality of our life during this time was phenomenal. John worked full-time, but to schedule vacations was challenging because they could not exceed 12 days due to clinical trial restrictions. (These are government regulated by design.) There were many times that John received a treatment and we left directly from the hospital for the airport. The hospital staff fully supported us by ensuring that the schedule for all the tests and treatments met the requirements of the clinical trials while allowing us to take advantage of so many travel opportunities. We knew in our hearts that these were going to be our retirement years and we were going to make the most of them.

We also knew that we were extremely fortunate that we had planned to travel during our retirement and had the financial resources to do it now. Since John's diagnosis, we already had been to China, Greece, Yellowstone and the Grand Tetons, Vancouver and the Canadian Rockies, Rome and the Amalfi Coast, and now the Baltic cruise that took us to 11 countries in 14 days.

CHAPTER

13

Disappointing Results: What Is Next?

The very least you can do in your life is figure out what you hope for. And the most you can do is live inside that hope. Not admire it from a distance but live right in it, under its roof.

— Barbara Kingsolver, *Animal Dreams*

In late June while on our Baltic cruise, John said to me, "I am having a problem with my vision in one eye. It sometimes appears blurry." I was concerned but suggested, "Perhaps you need to get your vision checked when we get back." If the problem had been persistent, I think I would have been more alarmed, but obviously he was the one who was dealing with the symptoms.

On other occasions during the cruise he said, "I don't want to be complaining, but I have a sore throat that has been hurting off and on." This definitely raised a red flag to me. I checked his throat and it did look red, but not white, which might suggest a strep infection. In an attempt to be more optimistic than I felt, I suggested that perhaps it might be an irritation due to the air on the ship. He was more fatigued than usual, but he attributed it to the change in activity level due to travel. We both knew that these symptoms could be related to his cancer, and yet we did our best to live in the moment and enjoy the opportunity that we had to take this wonderful trip together. Although we had been very open with one another and shared our hopes and fears throughout this cancer journey, I think we both had a sense of foreboding, without admitting it to one another, that this would most likely be our last big trip together.

When we returned home John told the oncologist of his symptoms. Because none of the conditions were constant, the doctor said that we would determine if they were related to his cancer when he had his scheduled scans in a few weeks. The waiting began again!

It has been mentioned several times, but it bears repeating: Waiting—whether it be for the next step for each stage of treatment, side effects from treatments, procedures, or results—is a humbling and stressful experience for the most patient of patients. Time seems to pass so slowly. And yet you feel like a top spinning out of control because you have no control.

During the long waits of days, weeks, and months we found the best way to cope was to put the burden of living with a chronic disease into God's hands and pray that we would accept the outcome. With practice, we learned to stay in the moment and take each day, each hour, and sometimes each minute as a gift of time. By transferring the burden, it allowed us to see the light of hope demonstrated through small gestures of kindness and love that crossed our paths.

Each day we learned to appreciate the true goodness of so many people; some who would remain strangers. However, we both believed that there were no coincidences and that these gestures of compassion were God's answer to our prayers that He was listening to us.

—ɱ—

July 31, 2012

Dear Family and Friends:

Today we learned that John would be starting a new chapter in his cancer journey. The scans taken in early June indicated some growth; the scans taken this past week showed additional growth and some new sites. Overall, the total growth is still 25 percent less than when he started, but because the growth has increased more than 20 percent from its lowest point, it appears that MDX-1106 is no longer benefiting him.

Clearly, we were disappointed, but we have been unbelievably blessed to have almost three years of the metastatic cancer sites under control. John was diagnosed four years ago this September and the odds he was given were six months to a year. The best news we got today is that the cancer has not spread to his brain and that we still have several possible treatment plans.

Our oncologist offered us four options. The most compelling choice is Yervoy, the FDA approved drug that had been previously suggested to us as a possible treatment. Although this drug carries more serious side effects to the autoimmune system, there is a real possibility that this could provide for years of positive response. The treatment consists of four infusions over a period of 12 weeks. Because of the potential for side effects, patients are monitored much more closely, and we will have to go into the hospital weekly. Treatment can continue over the 12 weeks dependent on how well John tolerates the drug. Some patients have little or no side effects. The doctor continues to offer us great hope and faith that this is just another chapter to be gotten through in what we hope to be a long book.

All of our caregivers at MGH, starting with the receptionist, were unbelievably supportive. They truly do treat us so compassionately. It would be a lot easier to be angry at the situation if we did not have this overwhelmingly supportive extended family.

This summer, John renewed his agreement to continue to work at Spellman. In September, he will start his 58th "first day of school." Each year is filled with fresh new hope and a sense of excitement for what can happen within the school community.

We told the doctor that John had just purchased some new back-to-school suits. The doctor said we could go ahead and cut off the tags and continue to "buy green bananas."

We are living life to the fullest with cancer as a chronic condition. Every day is a gift and we feel that our life continues to be blessed. We never take for granted all the good wishes and prayers that you have offered on our behalf.

It is a new chapter in our journey but we have many more to live and to share. Thank you for reading along with us and for your unique role in our journey....

Love,

Margaret and John

—⚹—

During the summer of 2012, John insisted that we make two purchases that I felt were not necessary at the time. The first was a new computer. Our desktop computer was about five years old. It was functioning, but it was operating very slowly. John really wanted us to convert to a Mac laptop because we now were both using iPhones and the iPad. It simplifies the integration of information, but it meant I was going to have to convert from using the platform of a PC, which was what I had used while I was working.

The second purchase was a new car. At the time, I had a Toyota Camry that was only six years old with less than 100,000 miles. He insisted that he thought we should make the purchase while he was still working full time. He said it would give us reliable transportation in and out of Boston and for our retirement. I remember picking up the car the day before his birthday and saying to him, "It's your birthday but I am getting the big present." He said, "You know that this is for the benefit of both of us."

More important than what he said was what he did not say at the time. He thought he was being so clever with the excuses he made to make these purchases during that summer. Always planning ahead, he wanted to ensure that I had been taken care of. I knew in my heart that he wanted these purchases in place before his health deteriorated any further.

September 25, 2012

Dear Family and Friends:

The chapters to our cancer journey this summer will be written as a series of emotional highs and lows. We were thrilled when John was allowed back on the clinical trial drug that had been previously successful, but he did not respond positively to the drug this time. In fact, scan results showed some new growth and new sites, so we needed to

choose a new treatment plan. In early August, we
decided to pursue the approved drug Yervoy. This
is the drug that is related to the clinical trial
drug that had been so successful for John, so we
are very optimistic. We were ready to start treatments fully aware that this drug could cause some
serious side effects.

In the meantime, John had developed two complications that needed to be evaluated by special-
ists at Massachusetts Eye and Ear Hospital. The
first issue was that John was having problems with
the vision in one eye. We visited an eye specialist
at Massachusetts Eye and Ear, and after hours of
testing, it was determined that he had leaky blood
vessels in his eye obstructing his vision. To treat
this problem would require a series of four injections into the eye. He received one and this one
treatment helped improve his vision. However, the
concern is that the drug used to clear his vision
is counterproductive to his melanoma treatment.
The eye specialist and our oncologist had several
consultations and finally agreed that John should
suspend the eye treatments and receive the melanoma treatments. John was not sorry to put off the
injections! All of this took two weeks of anxious
but hopeful waiting.

It has been determined that the second complication of swollen tonsils and lymph glands are
new cancer sites. A biopsy of the glands indicated
that the cancer is melanoma and that the tonsils
need to be removed surgically. The good news is
that the oncologist would not have approved the
surgery if he did not feel that John would benefit
from it and ultimately benefit from the drug. So
we were mentally prepared for the surgery to take

place tomorrow. Instead, we received a call yesterday saying that the surgeon was double-booked and an operating room would not be available until October 5th. We look forward to getting the surgery behind us and confirmation that we can continue on the current treatment plan.

We have done a lot of self-talk and praying during all of this. Again, it comes down to the fact that we have great faith that God will give us the strength to accept these new challenges. We have a very competent, compassionate medical team working on our behalf. And we know that we can continue to rely on our tremendous support system of family and friends to accompany us on this journey.

Thank you for your continued support and prayers.

Love,

Margaret and John

Anytime someone faces surgery you mentally prepare yourself for what you are about to experience. No one wants to have surgery, but a phone call like the one we received about delaying the surgery adds anxiety to an already stressful situation. I hung up the phone after the call from the surgeon's office and just looked at John. He was so crestfallen. I said, "The surgery will happen, just not tomorrow." He said, "I know, but now I have even less time to recuperate before our trip to Hawaii."

CHAPTER

14

If Not Now, When?

If you can't change your fate, change your attitude.
—Amy Tan

Prior to all of the recent health complications, we had planned a trip to Hawaii to celebrate our 40th wedding anniversary. Because we had raved about previous visits to the island of Kauai, high school classmates, Jane and Ed Leonard, wanted to share in the experience. Even before the change in the surgery date, I really felt the journey would be too taxing for John. I told him, "You have played this cancer card one time too many." But he was determined to go. He said, "If we don't go now, I don't know when we could go."

Because of the overbooked operating room schedule, John's tonsillectomy had been delayed by 11 days—that meant our departure date for Hawaii was planned just three weeks after his surgery. Needless to say, this added additional stress to our travel plans. I remember one of his oncology nurses saying to him regarding our plans, "John, you are still going to be in the United States. If you run into any complications you get yourself to a hospital and let them know you are a patient of Mass General. We can communicate directly with the medical staff by phone or Skype and coordinate your care." I just looked at her and said, "He doesn't need any cheerleaders to encourage him to travel. You are not making this any easier on me!"

If we had not planned to go with the other couple, I do not know that I would have agreed to go. But it was one of John's reasons why he wanted to go, and he did not want to disappoint our friends, even though they could have gone on their own. From my perspective, I would appreciate having the help available immediately if I needed it.

The expected recovery time from the surgery was at least four to six weeks and we were on week three. Ever the optimist, John kept telling me that his recovery would be even faster in the beautiful surroundings of Hawaii. The day of our departure, John's throat was still very sore. He had not eaten much solid food because it was hard to swallow and he was still weak. John dragged himself through Logan Airport to take the 12-hour flight to Hawaii. It was a strenuous ordeal, but he rallied a bit when we arrived on Kauai. He decided to spend the next day relaxing and then joined us for dinner.

At the end of a wonderful meal at one of our favorite restaurants the manager came over to our table and asked, "Did you enjoy your meal?" We all enthusiastically responded yes. I was even more delighted that John had actually been able to eat and enjoy the company of our friends. Naturally the manager was pleased with our response but then asked, "Are you staying close by?"

We thought she was just being conversational. We said, "We are at the Marriott in Lihue."

"I am sorry to be the bearer of bad news but there is a tsunami evacuation on the island. You could return to your hotel or you may want to consider driving inland away from the coast," she said.

Our hotel that was located right on the beach. It would be a seven-mile drive going south along the main evacuation route. Did we really want to return to our room on the 12th floor? We all agreed it would be safer to drive inland to a shelter, even though it was expected to bring us another 30 minutes further north away from the hotel.

The irony was that we were directed to a middle school on the island that was built on higher ground to serve the dual purpose of a school and evacuation shelter. The people at the school were very gracious, as Hawaiians are known to be, but John was not comfortable sitting on cafeteria-style benches in a school. Our friend Ed left his wife and us sitting in the cafeteria for about a half hour. We did not know where he had gone. We were laughing that he was known to drift and we always needed a leash for him.

When he returned he told us that he had gone out to the parking lot to talk with one of the policemen on duty. Ed told the officer that he was accompanying his friend who was in a compromised medical condition because he was recovering from recent cancer surgery. He further explained that we had just flown in from Boston the day before.

Our friend Ed had asked if it would be possible to move our van to the front of the line of traffic so that when the roads opened we would be able to get back to the hotel as soon as possible. John and I were so touched by Ed's kindness and forethought. We returned to the van to allow John to stretch out as best he could until the roads were opened. Roads were closed for the next four hours.

The good news was that we were spared the tsunami. The bad news was that by the time we were able to return to our hotel, according to our jet-lagged body time, it was seven o'clock on the morning of the third day of our trip. Needless to say, John was forced to spend the third day relaxing around the hotel. In the end, we enjoyed ourselves, but there were several anxious moments for me on this "vacation."

—๛—

Excerpt from John's Thanksgiving Faculty Letter 2012

Over the past few weeks, I have received many wonderful cards and notes that have meant a great deal to me. There were days ... and nights ... in the past that left me overwhelmed, frustrated, and wondering what was really happening to me. It was those cards, notes, and—most importantly—prayers that helped to keep me positive and focused on getting better.

One of my favorite cards came from my sister-in-law, Eileen, whose message read: "Sometimes the only sense you can make out of life is a sense of humor." And inside read, "With your positive outlook, upbeat energy, and sense of humor, I know you'll see your way through this. I believe in you." This card and its optimistic message hit a nerve with me. I knew I had to stop wallowing in the illness and begin to focus on my attitude that had kept me strong earlier. I can get better ... but I have to want to make it happen, and I can't forget that some things, even illness, can be laughable at times. I have to believe in myself and that, with God's help, I can get better.

I missed work terribly and my wife and I had "words" about when I could come back to Spellman, for how long, and even when I could drive. I have to admit now that in some cases it was too soon. I really wanted to attend the Mass on October 18. Not only could I not stand through most of the Mass, when I called my wife to pick me up after Mass, I was so sick that I had to have her stop the car and I left "breakfast" on someone's lawn.

Being able to attend the Mass on November 15 was a great privilege. It was a memorable day for all of us. I have to admit, though, I got special goose bumps during the Prayers of the Faithful when I heard the prayer that the school was thankful for my return to Spellman. That exactly was my prayer too.

I have much to be thankful for this year: my wife, my family, my health, and my dreams for the future. But, more now than ever, I am thankful to be part of the Spellman family. I missed the day-to-day, give-and-take of the first few months of school. I was connected by e-mail and phone but not by the smiles and goodwill that you have to see in person. I am thankful that our school is thriving, and I believe we have a strong, vibrant future as a great Catholic school that really "walks the walk" of Catholic identity.

I have been proud to be a part of Cardinal Spellman High School over the past fifty years, but I am most proud of where we are today and of the wonderful work that goes on in all of our classrooms every day. It is great to be at Spellman, and I look forward to the days, months, and years we have to work together.

I wish you and your family the most wonderful of Thanksgivings and a great time to be together and to count the blessings we all share.

John

Christmas 2012

Holiday greetings!

We hope that you and your families will enjoy the spirit of the season and the prospect of hope that each New Year brings.

We have some wonderful new travel memories for 2012. All of our children and grandchildren vacationed together in the Outer Banks. We rented a house on the beach and had a great time surfing the waves, building sandcastles, and flying kites. We managed our annual trip to Vermont with Heather and her family and Julie and Greg. Fortunately, we didn't suffer any damage or long-term power outages from Hurricane Sandy, but we experienced our first tsunami evacuation when were visiting Hawaii. One experience that you never want to add to your bucket list!

John and I took a wonderful cruise to the Baltic. We visited 11 countries in 14 days with the luxury of not having to pack and unpack. It was an incredible firsthand history lesson of what it was like to live in Eastern Europe during World War II, then under Nazi rule and Communism. The people who live in these countries have every right to feel proud of how they have rebuilt their cities, small towns, their economy and their entire way of living since the Cold War ended just 20 years ago.

As all of you know who have grandchildren, being a grandparent is the reward for raising a family. The joys of exploration, fascination, and learning are truly a pleasure when you don't have to worry about the day-to-day responsibilities of child-rearing. We have four grandchildren ranging in age from 18 months to eight years old. They never cease to amaze and delight us. Julie and Greg are expecting their first baby in April. This has been an answer to many prayers as they had a difficult year of miscarriages and loss.

John continues to defy the odds of his prognosis from more than four years ago. The word "patience" has taken on a whole new dimension for our entire family. We have been through a pretty rough stretch, but the important thing is we got through it and scans just this past week show that there has been a mixed response with the Yervoy treatments. The doctor said we have to give the drug time to see if it is working.

We never know how long we can stay on course with a treatment plan, but we are forever optimistic that John will continue this journey with the best possible medical care and opportunities for treatment that are available. His faith, spirit, and determination are amazing. We firmly believe that the extra magic in our lives has been our faith and trust in God and the extraordinary love, support, and continued prayers offered by all of you.

Like everyone, we have experienced ups and downs in this journey of life. Again this year, John and I never lose sight of how blessed we continue to be. This month we are celebrating our 40th wedding anniversary: a milestone for so many different reasons. So again, there is much to celebrate this year and we do ... every day! We continue to thank God for the opportunity to live with this disease and in doing so enjoy living life to its fullest.

May you all believe in the "magic" of the season and the hope that the New Year brings.

Love,

Margaret and John

In early December of 2012, Chris and Liz were coming home to attend a wedding. John and I planned to host a Christmas party during their visit because it would be the only time the whole family could be together. John had arranged a very special surprise for our four grandchildren and extended the invitation to my sister's two grandchildren to join us.

After dinner, we saw headlights coming down the driveway. John said, "Who could this be?" The excited kids, ranging in age from eighteen months to eight years old, ran to the windows just in time to see Santa Claus getting out of a pickup truck. All of the kids' eyes lit up. When we met him at the front door, Santa explained he could not come by sleigh because one of the reindeer had a cold and he wanted him to rest up in time for his Christmas deliveries. There were varying degrees of excitement and shyness as the kids looked at the big guy himself.

After some brief introductions, Santa sat down in an armchair and read aloud in a soft but commanding voice, "T'was the Night Before Christmas." He held everyone's attention including the very youngest. The parents and grandparents could not believe how well-behaved and attentive the children were.

When he finished reading the story, Santa told the children, "I have something special for each of you." From his big red sack, he pulled out a wrapped gift "personally" selected for them. Each child received a book. Santa stressed to the children how important it was to appreciate books and to learn to read.

John was overjoyed with how well the party had gone. He was as excited as the kids had been and told me, as he was getting ready for bed, "This is the best Christmas ever." Little did we know that it would be his last. Once again, it is a reminder to celebrate every day that we can and make memories for our families and ourselves.

The most magical memory for me occurred about two years after the party. Our then three-and-a-half-year-old grandson, Trenton, was standing beside the armchair that Santa Claus had occupied and said to me, "Grammy, Santa Claus sat in this chair."

I looked at him in disbelief. I said, "Trent, are you sure?"

"Yes, Grammy, he did and Grandpa was here too." Trent was 18 months old when Santa Claus made his special visit to our house and John had died five months later, just before Trent's second birthday. You never know what a child may comprehend or understand at a very young age!

As the years go by and the grandchildren take out their collection of Christmas stories during the holidays, they will point to the special book Santa Claus gave to them. This recollection always makes me smile because I share in their feeling of joy and the memory of how happy John was that night.

15

One More Obstacle

It's not whether you get knocked down;
it's whether you get up.
—Vince Lombardi

———⚬———

January 20, 2013

Dear Family and Friends:

John has never seemed to have totally regained his energy level since the surgery in October. He has been working, but he always has a general feeling of malaise. We have been watching him very carefully for side effects from the treatment he has been on because one of the most common problems with the drug is a weakening of the intestinal wall.

The medical team had been monitoring his hematocrit level, which measures the volume of red blood cells in the blood. The tests confirmed that he needed a blood transfusion. Not the solution to the whole problem but a fix.

As a result of the transfusion, he had his two best days in six months at work on Thursday and Friday. But Friday night he had severe pain across his abdomen and he ran a temperature. I brought him early Saturday morning to Mass General's Emergency Department; he was in the operating room by noon.

He did not present himself as the "typical" patient with a serious abdominal problem, but then again John is never "typical." God was watching over us because once they opened him up they found three melanoma tumors, two of which had perforated the colon and one more that was "impending." John has come through the surgery fine but the next two days are critical because of the chances of infection.

His spirits are good, but it is difficult to face another period of recovery from surgery.

We had finally made some plans to travel again this winter and spring. Knowing John, the only trip we definitely won't be taking is the one to Charlotte next week. Even he won't fight me on that one. The rest will be a wait and see. It gives us something to look forward to.

We have had a serious setback but John was reminding our oncologist just last week that he was initially diagnosed five years ago this May. The doctor's comeback was "And, I am not done with you yet."

We are not sure what will happen after John recovers from the surgery but we know that we can count on you for your prayers and support.

Love,

Margaret

—〰—

During the interview on admission to the Emergency Department (ED), we were asked if John had ever experienced similar severe abdominal pain. John told them emphatically that he had never suffered anything like these symptoms before. From their tone of voice and tense body language I could tell that the staff considered John's condition very serious. After further evaluation and consultation, the doctors recommended that John have surgery to determine the cause and provide relief from the pain in his abdomen.

Physicians take an oath to help patients to the best of their ability. In the case of a terminally ill or elderly patient, it is highly recommended that decisions related to the end of life treatment plan be discussed ahead of time with the patient, the patient's health care proxy, and family members so that the patient's wishes are known and recorded. These are difficult conversations but they are so helpful to the patient and the family when the time comes.

As John was lying in the Emergency Department bed with me seated next to him, the medical staff looked to me and said, "Before John consents to surgery, you need to know that your husband is gravely ill. We would like you to confirm that both of you understand and agree that you want us to honor his previously signed medical DNR order and the request that no extraordinary life-sustaining treatments be given, if the situation presents itself during surgery." DNR, or Do Not Resuscitate, is a medical order not to administer CPR or Cardiopulmonary Resuscitation and "extraordinary life-sustaining treatment" is any medical procedure given to a terminally ill patient that will prolong his life.

These pre-signed agreements do not mean that a patient is refusing palliative care which allows for physical comfort measures, i.e. pain relief. John was fully cognizant of what they were asking us, and he squeezed my hand as

144 Every Day Is a Gift

he looked to me for confirmation and agreement. He then turned to them and said, "Yes, we understand what you are asking us and what I have agreed to. I want you to honor my written requests." His goal was quality of life not quantity. Knowing that these were his wishes, I wanted the medical staff to carry them out but it was still difficult for me to corroborate.

—ɯ—

January 25, 2013

Dear Family and Friends:

It was one week ago tonight that John first experienced the pain that led to emergency abdominal surgery. He is making steady progress, but he must reach certain benchmarks before he can be released from the hospital. Hopefully, that will be some time this weekend. He will advance from a clear liquid diet to full liquids in the next few days. It is remarkable that even a bottle of Ensure can be appealing.

In another week, John will return for a follow-up with the surgeon. We hope the pathological report will be available at that time. This will tell us whether the cancer sites that were surgically removed had been metastasizing or if they were a side effect to the treatment John had been on. Together, the surgeon and our oncologist will decide what the next steps will be. Most likely, the scans that were scheduled for the beginning of February will be delayed.

Speaking of our oncologist, his compassion is incomparable. He walked right into John's hospital room, sat down on the edge of the bed and spoke with him about how concerned he was. His comment was: "John, you never seem to cease to amaze us!" It is so reassuring to know our doctor works closely with our surgeon and that together they will decide what we might anticipate in the future.

In addition to the doctor, three other people from the outpatient oncology staff came over at lunchtime to say a quick hello. They brought a big smile to his face and tears to his eyes. And finally, our outpatient nurse who has administered almost all of John's treatments at the MGH Infusion Center took the time after working a 12-hour shift to come to John's hospital room. She is and has been a major part of John's very special team of health care providers.

John even had a surprise visit from a specially trained and certified three-year-old Portuguese Water Spaniel named "Leoh." (The spelling is correct but the irony is that John's confirmation name is Leo, after his father.) He was such a gentle dog who at 54 pounds sat in his owner's lap like a baby. The owner is a volunteer who has been visiting patients with her pets for over 35 years.

Although the visits from MGH staff were very special, John is still more comfortable visiting with people at home. He appreciates all of the prayers, cards, and e-mails he has received.

So it has been a difficult week but we have certainly felt God's presence by the love that surrounds us. We feel so blessed to have you in our lives to share our journey.

Love,

Margaret and John

Prior to the emergency surgery, we were told that there was a possibility that John may need a colostomy to repair the walls of his intestine. Immediately after the surgery, the doctor confirmed that he was forced to give John a temporary colostomy to allow the bowel to heal from the perforations caused by the cancer sites. Barring any additional stress on the bowel, a common side effect of drugs he had been on, John would have reversal surgery in eight to 12 weeks. John understood that this was life-saving surgery, but this setback was both physically and emotionally draining for him.

When we met with the surgeon at John's post-op visit, the surgeon again asked John, "Are you sure you never experienced the kind of pain you had on admission to the hospital?" John answered, "I had physical discomfort the weekend before the surgery following dinner at a restaurant celebrating our daughter's birthday. I just attributed it to the unusually rich food I had eaten." The doctor said, "No, I am not talking about discomfort. When I operated, I found a healed perforation in your bowel that indicated it had burst some time two to three months ago. I can't believe you suffered this perforation and were not aware of the pain it would cause."

John and I put our heads together and the only conclusion that we could draw was that the perforation must have occurred when John was on pain medication for his tonsillectomy three months before. The pain related to the perforation would explain the general feeling of weakness that he had felt while recovering from the tonsillectomy and the need for the extended recuperation time following that surgery. The doctor agreed with us that this time frame would have been more in line with the healing that he had observed. In November, we had traveled to Hawaii only three weeks after his tonsillectomy. And now we understood that he must have been suffering from a perforation in his bowel. He was a very lucky man not to have suffered a systemic infection.

They say that pain and bleeding are the two primary reasons that force people to seek medical attention. In a situation where pain is masked because of a prescribed medication, you may experience a complication that you are not even aware of.

After the abdominal surgery was the first time since the Interleukin-2 treatments three years before that I saw John's spirit decline. I kept reminding him that it was temporary and that it was just one more bump in the road. In the meantime, he needed blood transfusions at least once, sometimes twice a week, and he needed to be intravenously hydrated regularly. We hoped that with the healing of the bowel, that his blood counts would improve, which would eliminate the need for transfusions. Scans were scheduled for late March and the appointment was set for April 2 to talk with the surgeon confirming that he could proceed with the reversal. Although John did not object to informing people who received our e-mails about the surgery, he did not want to share that he had had a colostomy.

January 31, 2013

Dear Family and Friends,

John finally made it home today after a 13-day stay at Mass General where he was recovering from emergency abdominal surgery. We certainly have had better physical accommodations and food during a stay in Boston for a lot less money, but we could not have asked for better or more compassionate medical care. John is doing well and now has to concentrate on getting stronger.

We are trying to work out what the next steps will be and which appointments we need to keep next

week and which ones will be cancelled. What we do
know is that for the rest of today and tomorrow we
don't need to be anywhere at any time. So it sounds
like a mini vacation to us.

Thank you all for your kind thoughts, prayers,
cards, and e-mails. It has helped to sustain us
through a pretty big bump in the road.

We are getting set to blaze new trails …
together.

Love,

Margaret and John

Little did I know what trails we would blaze! Just a week
after we arrived home from the hospital, we were hit with
the Blizzard of 2013. Boston received more than two feet
of snow and hurricane force winds. We lost power for four
days. We did everything that we could to stay warm, but
after two and a half days in a cold house, I called around
on my cell phone to find a hotel room with heat. We finally
found a place not far from home that had a room available.

As part of John's recuperation in the hospital, he had
received instruction from a wound nurse on how to care
for his colostomy. It was one of the very few times that
I witnessed John refusing to learn something. He wanted
nothing to do with the process of caring for or changing
the colostomy bag. The nurse was very kind and patient and
recognized that he was resistant, but she remained firm that
he must learn how to do this independently. He kept saying
to her that "my wife will have to do it for me." I honestly
did not mind, but I knew that he should be doing this for
himself. How could he ever go anywhere or do anything
independently? On the other hand, I knew that this was
supposed to be a temporary solution so that his intestine
could recover from surgery.

I asked him what it was about the colostomy that bothered him so much. He said, "There are three things: I do not feel confident that I am replacing the bag properly. I just never know if the bag is going to work as it should, and I think people will look at me to see if they can see the bag beneath my pants." I reassured him that the bag was not at all noticeable.

It made me think of people I had known with breast cancer who had had mastectomies. They too expressed embarrassment that people were looking at their chest to see which breast was the artificial one. I understood that people could become hypersensitive about what they see as a flaw or disfigurement. I responded to John by saying what he had said to me so many times before, "Something or someone can only have power over you if you let it." He said, "I hate it when you throw back my own words to me!"

We were both inexperienced at changing John's colostomy bag and he was too embarrassed about the unpredictability of his condition to stay with even one of our children during the power outage. His bowel movements had been very unpredictable. This was an emotionally and physically difficult chapter of John's journey. Outpatient support is given when a patient is discharged with a colostomy to reinforce how to change the colostomy bag and how to order supplies, etc. We had an appointment with a visiting colostomy nurse scheduled for Monday morning in our home.

By calling home from the hotel room early Monday morning, we found out that power had been restored overnight because the answering machine picked up the call. When we arrived home, the temperature had already gone up from below 45 degrees to 60 degrees.

The colostomy visiting nurse happened to be a male nurse, which positively impacted John's home visit. The nurse was very pragmatic but sensitive ... just what John needed at the time.

16

Man Plans, God laughs

*We must be willing to let go of the life we
have planned, so as to have the life
that is waiting for us.*
—E.M. Forster

———⚏———

March 3, 2013
From John's "President's Update" e-mail to the
Spellman Faculty
Greetings:

It's been great to see a few of you in the halls over
the past few days. I have missed being at Spellman
more than you know. I am hoping that over the next
few weeks my attendance will be more regular. I
never thought that the second half of the year would
be even more challenging than the first. Beyond my
family, having Spellman to think and pray about
gives me a purpose and an incentive to get better.

With this in mind, though, I wanted to let you
know that last Monday I submitted a two-part letter
to the Board of Trustees. The first paragraph was my
resignation from my full-time position as President

of Spellman. It really was a reflection of my health and energy. I have always wanted to do a great job for the school and, although I have kept up with e-mails, phone calls, and paperwork in the hospital or at home, it's not the same. This part of the letter goes into effect on June 30, 2013.

Once I wrote that paragraph, I realized it was not what was best for Spellman. We have a new principal, who is doing a great job, but I would like to work with him more. We also have a new admissions director, who is also doing great but there is still much to do, especially with exchange students. We have not replaced our advancement director and we need to work on the transition to a new president, who probably should have some different skills that I do not have.

Therefore, I have offered the board, God willing, my willingness to work part-time as president in the 2013–2014 school year. It will be a great time to transition and to reinforce the changes we have made over the past four years. The board has agreed to this proposal and I am looking forward to continuing my work at Spellman, while, at the same time, making a smooth transition in leadership.

As always, I appreciate your prayers and support. The Spellman family is based on faith and a true commitment to excellence. I am proud to serve as your president and I assure you that we will have a smooth and meaningful transition. Thank you for all you do.

God bless,

John

———⬥———

Although we had a nine-day cold snap in January, the first

two months of 2013 started off with less snow than usual. During February, as mentioned earlier, we were hit with a blizzard that left over two feet of snow on the ground and power outages for several days. On Friday, March 9, the snow started slowly but kept accumulating so fast the plows could not keep up. Keeping the roads clear was next to impossible. Winter in New England can be challenging but for medically compromised people, it can be devastating!

—⟋⟍⟍—

March 10, 2013

Dear Family and Friends:

The plan was simple ... John was scheduled at Mass General for scans on Friday and a transfusion on Saturday. That was before the snowstorm.

On Friday morning, John had tried to get up at least three times to take a shower, but he was light-headed. He tried one more time and fortunately I was able to prevent a "crash landing." It was now time to call 911. Within minutes, with the snow continuing to fall, six Whitman EMTs and firefighters were on the scene. It became a bit crowded in the bathroom. One of the firefighters was a former student and recognized John as the "head professor" at Spellman. John's blood pressure was low and they wanted to get him to the hospital.

The problem now was how to get John from the upstairs bathroom out to the ambulance waiting in the street (a tenth of a mile away). The driveway had been plowed but because of the intensity of the storm, they could not get the ambulance down the driveway. The Fire Department called in a

Department of Public Works truck that proceeded to get stuck in what used to be a grassy area of the driveway. The EMTs decided a gurney was not going to work and that they would use a chair to carry John through the wind and snow. He was wrapped up in blankets. The crowning touch was a Patriot's knit cap that made the whole presentation look totally absurd.

The EMTs decided it was safer and more reasonable to go to Brockton Hospital and to keep communication open with Mass General. Brockton Hospital took John in with open arms and over the next couple of days completed the scans and the transfusions in order to address the low blood count levels. On Tuesday, the hope is that we will meet with our oncologist at Mass General to discuss the cause of the blood loss.

We always say, "thank God where we live and when we live" regarding our battle with cancer—even during the absurdity of a crazy blizzard and a King Tut impersonation. Somehow we get done what needs to get done.

Next week we should be getting more details on the status of the cancer. In the meantime, thank you for your continued prayers and support.

Love,

Margaret and John

March 13, 2013

Dear Family and Friends:

We just wanted to give you a quick update regarding our visit with our oncologist yesterday. Overall, it was a good day at MGH. However, as you can imagine one doctor's appointment leads to scheduling four others within the next week.

The good news is that from reading the scans taken at Brockton Hospital, our oncologist feels that John's cancer has stabilized. Of course, they want more scans to be certain, but we were happy that this was his initial evaluation of them.

Secondly, John's blood levels have increased several points, which means that the six units of blood that he received over the weekend have helped him to reestablish a more normal blood supply. However, now we have to have his blood drawn every three days to confirm that his own body is taking control of a regular, healthy level of demand.

The two big questions that remain are what caused this dangerously low blood loss that put a huge strain on his heart, and what is causing the ongoing pain in his abdomen. So we are not out of the woods yet, but we feel that we are starting to get things back in control.

We continue to be humbled by the number of caring people who provide an overwhelming network of support. Every one of them is a reflection of God's love in our lives. We can never thank you all enough for being there for us.

Every day is a gift; some are just better than others.

Love,

Margaret and John

Throughout the fall, Dr. Lawrence had told us that John's hematocrit levels, or red blood cell counts, were registering on the low side of the normal range and he wanted to monitor them closely. Three days before John's emergency surgery he received his first blood transfusion. This was a fortunate coincidence since low blood counts can negatively impact recovery. We hoped that the surgery would correct the internal bleeding.

However, following the surgery, John's blood counts continued to be low and he needed transfusions once, sometimes twice, a week. Because of his weakened condition, the doctor would not conduct exploratory surgery to determine the cause of this blood loss. Both John and I wondered how long the doctors would allow him to receive transfusions even though they were considered part of his medical care to minimize his pain. The options for medical and curative treatment were running out. We began to realize that melanoma might not be the direct cause of John's declining health.

CHAPTER

17

New Hope: Bridge Hospice

When you come to the end of your rope,
tie a knot in it and hang on.
—Thomas Jefferson

On April 2 we met together with John's oncologist and surgeon. They had decided together that John was not physically strong enough to undergo reversal surgery to re-suture his intestine and eliminate the need for the temporary colostomy. John was understandably very discouraged with this news.

When both doctors left the room, John just stared into space. I said, "The doctors may not be operating now but it does not mean they are giving up on you, John. They stated that you could not have the surgery now because it is too risky. If your condition improves, they may reconsider this decision." Dejectedly he responded, "Yeah, I know."

The doctors' decision not to operate meant, at the very least, that John would have to learn to adjust to having the colostomy for a longer period of time. Although John understood that the colostomy had saved his life, the need for it, from an emotional standpoint, was now negatively impacting his quality of life. He was disheartened and I could sense that he was not giving up hope, but may have to adjust to not living life as fully as he had been or wanted.

This was a low point of our cancer journey. We had not shared John's condition of having the colostomy with our friends and his colleagues because John felt it was too personal. This was why the e-mails had not disclosed this level of detail of his condition up to now.

However, we always had been very honest with our children about what was going on. After the consultation with the oncologist and the surgeon John said to me, "What are we going to tell the kids?" I said, "I think we should talk to each of them separately and tell them the truth. You are discouraged by the news, but you are not ready to give up yet."

When John was first diagnosed, our two grandchildren were ages three and one. They knew Grandpa had a lot of doctors' appointments and hospital visits to help him get better. Because John was able to function at such a high level most of the time, we did not feel we needed to be more explicit than that. Now the four grandchildren were eight, six, four, and almost two. John and I discussed his declining condition and agreed that the day might be coming that he would have to tell the grandchildren that he was sick and would not get better.

John's inclination was to use every situation as a teaching opportunity. He wanted to demonstrate that you live life fully, love with all your heart, and you leave this life with no regrets. Some days this was a very high expectation to meet ... even for John!

In early April, our daughter Julie and her husband Greg were expecting their first child. They lived about 45 minutes away from the hospital where she planned to deliver the baby and an hour from where she worked. Our house was only about 15 minutes away from the hospital

and 20 minutes from her work. Julie had had several miscarriages so John wanted to be sure that she was as close
as possible to medical care. They moved in with us on the
first of April.

On April 8, Julie and Greg had a very healthy baby
boy. It truly was a miracle after all they had been through
trying to have a child. The best part was that John and I
were able to visit them in the hospital on the baby's birthday
on our way home from Boston. Again the hospital staff at
Mass General tried to move us along in the queue so that
we could leave to visit our new grandson.

When we arrived at South Shore Hospital, John was
showing signs of weakness and fatigue and I suggested,
"Why don't we get a wheelchair and I can bring you to the
maternity floor?"

His pride and stubbornness got in the way. He said,
"No, I want to walk into the room under my own power."

"I could leave the wheelchair down the hall and you
could still walk into the room."

"I said no."

There is an image of him imprinted on my mind shuf-
fling down the long hallways to get to Julie's room. Once
he got in the doorway, he perked right up, walked right in
and found himself a chair. He was so pleased to visit the
new family and be there to personally welcome the birth of
our new grandchild.

During all of this time, John continued to work for
Spellman. He remained connected through e-mail, telephone, and meetings in his office when possible. Over
the years John had been actively involved in a student
recognition program for the Jostens Company called
Renaissance. The program was designed to acknowledge
students' success in improved academic performance, academic achievement, and even perfect attendance. John had
introduced the program while he served as an assistant

principal at Silver Lake Regional High School. At the time, the school had very few students making the honor roll. After the institution of the program, students worked much harder to achieve honor roll status, improve their grades, and attain perfect attendance. John's research on recognition of achievement through behavioral modification programs became the foundation for his doctoral dissertation.

Jostens invited John to join their national speakers' bureau to promote their program of student recognition. During his association with Jostens, he met an Emmy award-winning motivational speaker, humorist, and author named Mark Scharenbroich. Although they did not see each other often, Mark and John were respectful of each other's contribution to motivating students and became very good friends.

Mark was a recipient of the e-mails that I had been sending out so he knew what was going on, and would always send a note of encouragement to John. As a gift to John, he wanted to speak to the student body of Cardinal Spellman High School. He planned to come the day before April vacation started on April 12.

John really wanted to attend Mark's presentation and to see the teachers and students. Since he had lost so much weight, I had to go out and buy him a new pair of pants the night before just so he would look presentable. We arrived 45 minutes before the assembly was to start just so we could walk into the school auditorium and rest before the students arrived.

Mark gave a presentation on the value of friendship and what it meant to him to have become friends with John. He wanted the students to understand that friendships could be short-term or lifelong, but they were worth making and keeping. John was so moved by Mark's expression of kindness.

At the same assembly, John had the opportunity to address the student body and teachers to personally thank Mark for coming and especially for sharing his gift of offering a memorable presentation. Both John and I knew that this would probably be one of the last times he would address the student body as president of the school. His goal was to make it to graduation, and that was still six weeks away. With his declining health and lack of energy and stamina, it did not seem likely he would be able to attend.

John was not someone who saved many letters or cards. That is why it came as quite a surprise to me when I cleaned out his office and I found underneath his blotter a few inspirational notecards that Mark had written to him over the years. This demonstrated to me, and later I shared with Mark, just how much he inspired John and valued their special friendship.

April 20, 2013

Dear Family and Friends:

The events at the Boston Marathon this week have been tragically sad. They remind us that life is precious and our lives can suddenly change in a moment.

Living with a chronic disease has its challenges, but you do have the opportunity to evaluate what is really important in your life and how you choose to spend your time. John and I feel blessed that we have faith in God and confidence that He will give us the strength to accept His will, not ours.

We have said so many times how fortunate we are to have access to world-class medical care, treatment options, and compassionate caregivers.

John has participated in cutting-edge, clinical trials; some of which proved to be extremely successful in the quality of our life, and the participation in this research has contributed to the advancement in the treatment of melanoma.

What began as new challenges in John's cancer in August led to additional cancer surgery and an extremely arduous treatment in the fall that, in the end, proved unsuccessful. In January, complications from this treatment led to emergency surgery for a perforated bowel that resulted in a colostomy and an even more difficult recovery. John's fatigue was compounded with dramatic drops in blood chemistry to the point of severe anemia. During the March blizzard, he was transported by ambulance to a local hospital to receive blood transfusions over four days. Since that time, he has received bi-weekly hydrations and weekly blood transfusions. In the meantime, managing the pain has become even more difficult.

We knew that the options for treatment were getting fewer and the possibility of stabilizing and/or reducing the cancer sites was becoming less likely. Therefore, on Thursday, we talked with John's oncologist and we agreed that any remaining options to medically treat John's cancer would make him very sick and not significantly extend the quality of his life. A bridge hospice program is recommended as the next step; that will allow us to remain connected to Mass General, but we will start to receive some services at home as needed.

Throughout this school year, John continued to work. Due to his health complications, he will officially step down as President of Cardinal Spellman High School at the end of June.

When John was diagnosed five years ago, he expressed two wishes: to see our youngest daughter happily married and then hopefully to celebrate the birth of her first child. He walked Julie down the aisle during the summer of 2011 and on April 8, Julie and Greg had a healthy baby boy, Benjamin Thomas. We are blessed and proud of our three wonderful children, their spouses, and now five grandchildren.

For Christmas, John gave me a little sketch of Mickey Mouse and his gang of friends riding in an old jalopy that says: "The best part of life's journey is who you get to share it with." You have all been a tremendous source of support and we continue to feel the power of your prayers and love. It has been truly humbling to reconnect with so many former students, parents, colleagues, and old and new friends during this journey.

So, like so many others in Boston this week, we are reminded how important it is to spend quality time with our family and friends. And that is exactly what we plan to do in the time ahead. May God bless you for the strength you have given us on our ride in this "jalopy." Every day has been a gift!

Love,

Margaret and John

On April 16, the day following the Boston Marathon bombing, John had an appointment at the Yawkey Center at Mass General. Mass General was one of the hospitals where victims of the bombing were taken. We were aware that President Obama was planning to visit victims on the afternoon of John's appointment.

Naturally, there was heightened security and a sense of urgency throughout the hospital. As we were entering the parking garage, we had to prove that we had an appointment before they allowed us to enter. During our appointment, we learned that some of our nurses had friends who had treated victims, but everyone in the infusion center knew an oncology nurse and her husband who were among those who had lost a limb.

There is a long hallway in the Yawkey Building of Mass General that looks out to the street and to Boston's Back Bay area. It was very strange to look down on normally busy Cambridge Street and see that all the traffic had been diverted from the street and entrance to the hospital to allow President Obama to come to pay a visit to the victims and hospital staff who had treated them. It is so strange how the events of a single day can impact people so differently. To some the tragedy was a minor inconvenience but for so many, the events of the bombing will remain with them every day for the rest of their lives.

May 11, 2013

Dear Family and Friends:

Our jalopy ride took a bumpy turn last week, but we have found our way back to the main road.

Last weekend we had one more unplanned trip to Mass General. John's blood pressure was low, his heart rate high, his blood sugars erratic, and we just couldn't get his pain under control. He was admitted Sunday night, expecting to stay overnight, but it has taken all week to get the right mix of medications.

This hospital stay has been both a physical and emotional roller coaster. Earlier in the week, we thought we were going to have to choose between hospice and blood transfusions. Hospice provides palliative care in the home, which is where John would like to be. (Palliative care focuses on pain management and offers physical, mental, and spiritual support when dealing with a serious illness. It does not offer curative treatment but both types of care can be offered at the same time.)

But John seems to require blood transfusions to keep him comfortable. Blood transfusions only can be given in a hospital, and transfusions are not generally considered palliative care treatment. However, God has again blessed us because Old Colony Hospice has agreed to provide up to two transfusions a week at our local community hospital and hospice will provide the transport.

Our goals now are to get him home from the hospital, have him receive sufficient medication and blood transfusions to be comfortable, and to enjoy time with our family. John continues to fight with everything he has got to live life to the fullest every day. We are hoping that John will feel up to doing some writing, which he had hoped to do when he retired.

It has been a blessing to have our daughter, son-in-law, and their infant son living with us. Our son and his family are arriving today from Charlotte for an extended stay and our older daughter and her family live nearby. We will have our first Mother's Day together in many years. Next weekend we are celebrating our grandson's First Communion and our one-month old grandson's christening. As we have said so many times before, God is good all the time and every day is a gift.

Although this week has been a bumpy ride, you have all given us clear signs of love and support to continue this journey together.

Thank you all for your love and friendship,
Margaret and John

CHAPTER

18

A Final Gift

*No act of kindness, no matter how small,
is ever wasted.*

—**Aesop**

As John remained hospitalized during his unexpected
admission in May, we had several conversations
with social services about what physical and medical
accommodations would be provided if John could return
home. It was finally agreed that Old Colony Hospice would
come in several times during the week to check on him and
twice a week they would draw John's blood to determine
if he needed transfusions. They would arrange for a hospital bed, wheelchair, and other accommodations to assist
in John's physical care; they would also provide transport
to our local hospital for transfusions, if needed.

In the meantime, our children were making accommodations at home to convert our living room into a bedroom
equipped with a hospital bed. We knew that the number of
steps getting in to our house was going to be a challenge.
People were so willing help us get this all set up. Overnight
my sister and her husband arranged to get a portable

handicap ramp installed. In addition, a retired carpentry teacher and friend built and installed a wooden ramp to bridge the gap between the portable ramp and the top step in through the front door. Our children received the furniture and arranged it so that John would be on the first floor of the house but away from the hubbub of activity.

John was discharged on a Saturday morning and driven home by ambulance. Even with the handicap accommodations, it was a challenge to get John into the house, but we managed. I really did not know how many trips he was going to be able to make in and out because he was so weak.

During the spring, Chris visited as often as he could. He had come for a visit in March and could see that John's health was declining. He and his wife arranged to rent a house near the ocean for two weeks in May so that he could be close by for an extended stay. He drove up with his family from Charlotte and arrived for a visit with John at our house about an hour after we had come home from the hospital.

Although our grandchildren had had opportunities to visit John when he was in the hospital, we were happy that each of them could visit Grandpa in the comfortable surroundings of home. John felt it was very important for them to see him for themselves, especially now that he was in declining health. He wanted them to understand that he was too sick to get better.

Sometimes John would just let the kids crawl around on his bed, or when he was in the hospital they would visit him in his room but might not speak directly to him. They would make conversation about the construction site outside his window. He knew that they understood that he was sick and they, like many adults, did not know what to say under the circumstances. Being there was all that was important.

John's parents were separated when his father died alone in a house fire. John was only eight years old. As was often the custom at the time, he was not allowed to participate in the funeral services. He said that he truly never believed his father had died until he was about twelve. Some people, even now, choose not to expose children to death or dying at a very young age. We believed that death must be accepted as part of life. Any child who has had a relationship with a person will miss that individual if he is no longer present in the child's life. If the child can verbally communicate, it is important to try to offer an explanation of death that he can comprehend. It is equally important that the child be given an opportunity to ask questions.

About a month before John died, he knew the time had come that he had to talk to each of the grandchildren in terms that they would comprehend. I remember him saying to me, "Don't be surprised if they are angry at me because I am dying. I understand this is not what any of us wanted."

As he spoke with each of them separately, John made it very clear that just because he was sick, it did not mean that when they became sick in the future that they would die. He explained that all living things, dogs and birds and insects, die one day. We never know how long any of us will live but love never dies; it always lives on. This is the circle of life.

Our daughter, Heather, and son-in-law, Frank, had already told Zachary and Keira that Grandpa was not going to get better. The children have very different personalities and they reacted accordingly when John spoke to each of them separately. Zach at age eight was angry, and Keira, age six, just cried. After John spoke with four-year-old Max, he came out to me in the kitchen and said, "Do Zach and Keira know that Grandpa is dying? I don't think they do, I need to tell them." You never know how a child, or an adult for that matter, will react to this type of news.

After John died, our children felt that although these conversations were difficult and sad, the time the children had spent with John was beneficial in their acceptance of

Grandpa's death. The children could see for themselves that he was not well and that his body was "too sick to get better."

Often it is a small gesture of kindness that has the greatest impact. During one of our long clinical trial days at the hospital, Mohammedi, the receptionist, stopped by John's room and presented him with a small teddy bear. With a twinkle in her eye, she said, "You can give it to your grandchildren." John laughed appreciatively and said, "No, they can share it with me. "

When we arrived home from the hospital that day he put the teddy bear on his nightstand. Every time one of the grandkids came into our bedroom they would ask to play with his teddy bear. This stuffed animal prompted wonderful conversations and great memories between Grandpa and the grandkids.

After John's death, I never removed the teddy bear from the nightstand. Each time one of the children would come into the room they would ask, "Can I play with Grandpa's teddy bear?" Or if they were sleeping overnight they would ask, "Can I sleep with Grandpa's teddy bear?" Of course, the answer is always yes.

The teddy bear continues to objectify the relationship that John had with the grandchildren when he was alive and now that he is gone. The children can freely share their ideas about death or, in particular, ask questions about Grandpa's death depending on their age, understanding, and acceptance. "This belonged to my Grandpa. He died, you know!" Or, "Why did Grandpa's body have to stop working?" Or "I wish Grandpa didn't have to die. I miss him." Or, "I like that book but it makes me kind of sad because it reminds me of Grandpa."

These sentiments create the ideal teachable moments for the children to express their grief and for the adults to talk with them about their feelings. I know John would be very happy that "his" teddy bear continues to serve as a bridge to meaningful dialog about a difficult concept. Recently, I connected with Mohammedi to let her know how much our family continues to benefit from her thoughtful gift.

The day after John was discharged was Mother's Day and we enjoyed having the entire family over to visit. Our children's Mother's Day gift to me (and really to us) was a collection of Rick Steves' travel videos. The kids even purchased a TV set and a DVD player so that we could set it up and watch the DVDs together in the newly adapted space in the living room.

As it turned out, John and I did enjoy watching two of the Rick Steves' videos. But that was all. On Monday, the visiting nurse from hospice came to the house to draw John's blood. She was an experienced phlebotomist, but she was unsuccessful in accessing his veins. We called the hospital to ask what they would suggest that we do.

We told the oncology nurse practitioner at Mass General the problem that the hospice nurse had in accessing John's veins. We were aware of a drug that they had used at least one other time that helped in accessing John's veins to draw blood. This drug cannot be administered outside a hospital setting. The nurse practitioner recommended that we bring him directly into the infusion center rather than go to the Emergency Department because they knew John and had all of his records. Fortunately, our son was working from home that day so he was available to lift John into the wheelchair and get him into the car.

John had made it very clear to his doctor during his most recent hospital stay that he wanted to go home to be in familiar surroundings. John's oncologist agreed to release him. When he was called in to evaluate John's condition on Monday afternoon, he was surprised how weak John had become in just two days. He apologized for letting him go home. I told the doctor there was no apology necessary. It was John's wish to go home and he was able to do that.

Unfortunately, it just was not a long stay. John needed transfusions now on a regular basis. Bridge hospice required transportation to a hospital for the transfusions. When the doctor said that we would have to make alternative plans, John squeezed my hand. We knew the options had run out. Our children recognized that having John at home had been much more demanding than any of us had anticipated. I was sleeping on the couch near him. He was not mobile so whatever he needed I had to get for him. The alternative plans would require some type of hospice care in a facility. My dilemma was I did not know where I would be able to place him at five o'clock on a Monday afternoon. The infusion center closed at 8:00 p.m. every night. I felt overwhelmed with the task of finding hospice care for John at that time of day.

Dr. Lawrence immediately took charge and emphatically told the nurse that he expected the staff to find a bed for John in the hospice unit of the Lunder Building. (I did not even know they had a hospice care unit at the hospital.) The doctor made it very clear that he wanted this arrangement made as soon as possible. He did not want any delays in finding space for John.

Oddly enough, the construction of the Lunder Building with dedicated space for cancer treatments had started four years prior when John was in the hospital for his Interleukin-2 treatments. At the time of construction, I wondered if John would live long enough to see the inside of it.

Once again, Mass General staff and administration responded quickly and efficiently. Several of the oncology nurses who had treated John in the infusion center over the years volunteered to transport John to the Lunder Building.

The medical staff was so kind. I knew they were all sad to have to make this trip. They had done everything they could for him. They knew that this new room would be where John would be when he drew his last breath. John was still lucid, but was fading in and out of consciousness.

Once he was settled in, I asked, "Do you need anything?" He said, "No, I just need sleep and prayers." I asked the nurse on duty how she thought he was doing. She said she thought he was stable. Chris and his wife had come into the hospital with me. I decided that we should all go home for the night and try to get some sleep ourselves. Of course, the nurse knew to call me if anything changed.

The next day, Dr. Lawrence came in to see John. As he was leaving, he asked, "Are you planning to stay overnight at the hospital?" I told him I had not planned on it but if he thought I should then I certainly would. I honestly did not believe that John was so close to death. Dr. Lawrence said, "You might want to think about it." Our son, Chris, was with me at the time and he said, "I am staying with him, Mom." The hospital staff again was very accommodating and made arrangements so that we could both stay with John overnight in his room. He was somewhat restless, but his pain seemed to be under better control.

Early the next morning as the nurse attended to his needs, I asked how she thought he was doing, and she said she thought he seemed stable. But by 10:00 a.m. she said, "You know, he seems to be slipping, I think you should call your family in."

They say you can never accurately predict when a person is going to pass from this life into the next, but I truly believe John waited until all of our children and their spouses were able to get into the hospital to be with him. We were all there as he peacefully slipped away just before 2:00 p.m. on Wednesday, May 15, 2013. We all smiled knowing that John had probably beseeched God to wait until school was out for the day.

After John died, the nurse then suggested that each person might want to say a last good-bye alone. They arranged for us to have a room where we could all wait for our turn with him rather than having us stand out in a hallway.

Immediately after we had our final good-byes, the kids all got into a take-charge mode of who should be called and which one of them would make the call. I know John must have been so proud of them. They were all grieving but they were coping by finding something useful to do. At the same time, we started making the initial funeral arrangements.

Fortunately, in mid-April, John and I had done some preplanning by selecting the cemetery plot and visiting funeral homes. This was what he referred to as "reality shopping." One day we just drove around looking at cemeteries as if we were picking out a site to build a home, which I guess you could say was destined to be our final resting place. We visited several cemeteries, but we finally agreed on a lot that would accommodate two burial plots with well-maintained grounds.

Another day we visited the funeral homes. John wanted to take into consideration that there would be a lot of visitors and he wanted to be sure that there was adequate parking and easy access. One funeral home was adjacent to a school. Although he liked the facility, he did not want visitors to the funeral home or the school to be inconvenienced with traffic when school was let out for the day. Again, I remember just shaking my head in disbelief that he would even care about this.

When preplanning with a funeral home, it is left up to you how many details you want to decide ahead of time. One of the questions we were asked was if we knew how many days and hours we want to have for visiting. Right away John said, "I want the hours to be limited to one day and that I would like it to be scheduled to start at 3:00 p.m."

I asked, ""Why would we start at three and not four?"

His response was, "Teachers like to be able to go to

wakes right after school lets out so that they can go home from there."

Astounded, I said, "Really, John, this is not all about the teachers this time." He would hear none of that and told the funeral director, "The visiting hours would start at 3:00 p.m."

The funeral director patiently smiled and said, "I think that if you start at three, you are still going to have to go until 8:00 p.m. because this is going to be a large wake." John's response to that was, "They can do it."

Not only did John have an opinion about the times of the wake, he told me, "I want the wake on a Friday and the funeral on a Saturday so that the school schedule will not be disrupted." I looked at him incredulously and said, "Then you are going to have to work out with God that you die on a Monday or Tuesday so that we might be able to meet your scheduled plans!"

It goes without saying one of John's strengths as an administrator was that he was a planner. He was very conscious of the school's academic calendar and special events. In fact, he started dictating to me the points he wanted to make and a quote he wanted to include in his graduation speech while we were in the Emergency Department on May 5, ten days earlier. He even went so far as to suggest that, "If I cannot make this speech, I would like you to do it for me." I said, "John, you are being very presumptuous. What makes you think that you will not do everything that you can to be there? And if you cannot be there, I would not give this speech unless Spellman asked me to do it in your place."

When a person is chronically ill, you may prefer to deal with the illness privately. But we had to keep in mind that John was a well-known figure in several different area communities. He was still serving as the president of Cardinal Spellman High School. Graduation exercises, the culminating activity of the school year, were scheduled the next week. In making the funeral arrangements, I had to keep in mind that John had planned to involve several members of the teaching staff and the school choir to play an integral role in the funeral service. He had already discussed and agreed on the music selections with the choir director. My family and I arranged the visiting hours and funeral around Baccalaureate services, senior awards night, and graduation.

There was a place in the graduation program for the president's address. John and I had told Spellman's principal that John had started his graduation speech while he was in the hospital. After John died, the principal reached out to me to ask if by chance John had finished the speech. I said, "No, but he had listed the bullet points that he had wanted to make, a quote he wanted to use, and I know the message that he had in mind to deliver." He said, "I am reluctant to ask but do you think you might be able to send me what you have and I will try to supplement the material if you need help? Oh, and by the way, we know it is a lot to ask, but do you think you could deliver the President's Address in John's place?"

I could just hear John whispering in my ear, "You can do this!" I said to the principal, "Even in death, John can create high expectations of me. I will probably never forgive myself if I do not follow through on this for him. I will do it." I got off the phone and said to myself, "What are you, crazy?"

———◈———

May 18, 2013

Dear Family and Friends:

As many of you know by now, John passed away peacefully on Wednesday afternoon with our family gathered around him. As he drifted in and out of consciousness in his final days, he had difficulty communicating. Frustrated, he finally folded his hands together and we knew he wanted us to pray with him and we did.

John was a registered organ donor. When John passed, I asked the attending physician if there was any chance any of his organs could be used. I was disappointed when he said no. Later, as we were driving home, we got a call from the New England Organ Bank telling us that perhaps John's corneas could be used. After an intensive interview of John's medical history, I was told he would be giving the gift of sight to two blind people. I was overjoyed to think that John, who was such a visionary, would be able to give someone the chance to see. This was the final gift of John's legacy.

A few weeks ago, we told you of a plaque John had given me for Christmas that depicted Mickey Mouse and his friends riding in an old jalopy. The inscription reads: "The best part of life's journey is who you get to share it with." John lived his life fully and he would want us to continue to celebrate our lives to the fullest. The best way to celebrate John's life is to continue to share the tales of your own jalopy rides with him, with us, and to celebrate new ones of your own.

John and I have been truly humbled by the outpouring of support and prayers we have received, particularly over these last five years. My children and I know that God will give us the strength to accept His will.

Thank you does not begin to express the gratitude we feel.

Love,
Margaret

The kids and I visited the funeral home the day after John died to finalize the arrangements. Our local church would only allow funerals at the scheduled morning mass time of 9:00 a.m. unless arrangements were made with a visiting priest. Fortunately, the deacon at Spellman helped to make arrangements so that we were able to have a priest who served on the board of trustees preside over the funeral mass at 10:30 a.m.

With all of the pre-planning decisions that John had made, it surprised me that he had not selected the readings that would be used during the mass. He had been in the seminary for four years and was far more familiar with the bible than I was. For some reason, he left this responsibility to me. Fortunately, again, I received help from the Spellman community to help me identify appropriate readings.

There are so many details in planning a funeral it can be overwhelming. Our children were so helpful to me during this time. Each one identified a task and followed through on the details. Chris had decided he wanted to find a function room to use for the collation that would be close to the cemetery since John was being buried immediately after the funeral.

The florist who had done the flowers for Julie's wedding offered to come to the house, which meant my daughters and I could make the selections together. My daughter-in-law took on the responsibility of putting the funeral program together and working out how they would be printed and brought to the church. My sons-in-law became the primary childcare providers and ran errands as needed.

We collected photos to be displayed at the funeral home and a Spellman student helped us put a video together. The staff at Whitman-Hanson also sent pictures and a video highlighting John's career at Whitman-Hanson. We brought the photos, many of John's awards, a scrapbook created by the Silver Lake staff, and a paper chain of well wishes made by the Spellman students earlier in the spring. My sister helped me to put together a playlist of John's favorite music.

The staff at the funeral home did a wonderful job of displaying the family photos taken during our vacations together, the awards, and they even showcased the students' paper chain between stanchions that guided people waiting in line. It was a beautiful tribute to this man. Even with five hours for visiting, many people waited in line for more than two hours to pay their respects.

The following day the church was overflowing. The principal of Spellman had arranged for student volunteers dressed in school uniform to serve as an honor guard as we processed in and out of the church. There must have been over one hundred students who lined the church steps to pay tribute to their president and a fellow alumnus.

The Liturgical Choir's voices were amazing. The students willingly offered their gift of music and song. It was a true celebration of life and John must have loved every minute of it.

Whitman-Hanson's technology department made arrangements at the church to set up a live video of the funeral so that the overflow crowd could watch the service from the church's lower hall. Everyone wanted to show their love and respect and they did, each in their own way.

During one of Chris' visits home that spring, John had asked him if he would be willing to give his eulogy. Chris said he was humbled to be asked but hoped he would be able to do it well. Later I found out that he had been working on it since John had asked him to do it. It was very unlike Chris to do anything ahead of time.

Chris gave a beautiful tribute to his father, and I know that John was very proud of the job our son did. One particularly touching recollection was how John would mark special days for our family, both happy and especially sad, by eating ice cream. Chris encouraged everyone at the funeral to eat ice cream that day and think fondly of John. We served it for dessert following his funeral. Many times since John's funeral, people who attended have told me that, they too, now mark days of joy and sadness by eating ice cream and think fondly of John.

After the funeral was over and people had left the collation, the kids agreed to go back to the funeral home to pick up the photos and awards while I went home to edit the graduation speech that I had to deliver the next day!

This is an excerpt from the president's address at Cardinal Spellman High School's Graduation on May 23, 2013:

> When John left his teaching position at Spellman in 1977, the students presented him with a plate that reflected his personal philosophy: "I shall not pass this way again. I expect to pass through this world but once. Any good thing, therefore, that I can do or any kindness I can show to any fellow human being let me do it now, let me not defer nor neglect it, for I shall not pass this way again."
>
> Well, John was honored and humbled to be called back to Spellman four years ago to serve as your president as you started your high school journey … when you live with the daily reality and reminder that life here on earth is fragile and limited, you gain a new perspective to live each day to its fullest. God's greatest gift to us is the gift of life itself. So, go out there and become the person you are meant to be. Go out there and live a life of passion and purpose. And take it from someone who has lived to make every day count!

19

Life After Death

Everything has its wonders, even darkness
and silence, and I learn
whatever state I am in, therein to be content.
—Helen Keller

June 6, 2013

Dear Family and Friends:

It has been three weeks and one day since John passed away. The hectic pace of planning the funeral services has quieted, and the finality of how we have to adapt to life going forward has set in. All of the counselors and books on grieving tell you that everybody grieves in their own way and in their own time. I would agree with this statement.

Our eight-year-old grandson announced to his mother today that he was not going to be sad anymore about missing Grandpa. When his mother asked why not, he said, "Now Grandpa is always in my heart and he is no longer sick from cancer."

Although I would agree with Zachary in his thought process, the rest of us have some catching up to do about not being sad. I do believe that our children and their families are doing well. God has blessed each of us with an understanding that it was John's time to leave us in body but not in spirit. Thank you all who during your visits at the wake, attendance at the funeral, or through a card, letter, or e-mail have shared with us your "John" stories. They truly are a source of joy and comfort.

In today's *Boston Globe*, an expanded obituary was written. I wanted to share it with you if you hadn't seen it. It captures some of John's accomplishments, but it does not reflect his contagious laugh, his joy of life, his love of family, friends, students, and colleagues, or his belief that every day is a gift to be lived fully.

So, we are doing our best to remember his unique spirit and follow his lead by living in the present, looking to happy days in the future and continuing to share your stories with us about your "jalopy rides" with John.

Love,

Margaret

―⁂―

Before John died, we had agreed that Heather and Frank would be given his Jeep. He had informed Heather of our decision. A couple of weeks after he died, Heather and I arranged to meet up at the Registry of Motor Vehicles to turn in his license plates and transfer the title. I was running a little late so I called her on my cell phone to let her know. She sounded emotional when she answered the phone. I understood that transferring the title of John's car over to her was a symbolic confirmation that John was no longer with us and might cause her to be upset. I asked, "Is something else bothering you besides transferring the title?" She answered, "I have been trying to remove the license plates from the car and the screws are rusted so I cannot get them off." Naturally, I understood why this would be frustrating, not to mention indicative of some higher interference with trying to get the job done. As I was talking with her on the cell phone, both of us heard unexplainable church bells ringing. I said, "Heather, do you hear those bells?" She answered, "I sure do!"

I knew the RMV was not near a church and I was not driving by one. I said to her, "Heather, your father is ringing our bells. He is letting you know that he is around and that everything is going to work out." It did.

Grieving for someone you love who has been your life partner and best friend is overwhelmingly sad. You miss the person and your daily interactions with them. I was unprepared for the two other losses that occurred at the same time, which are explained in the following paragraphs.

For five years, John and I had spent many hours and days together: driving, waiting for office visits, treatment rooms, treatments, X-rays or scans. His schedule dictated mine as well. To maximize the time, John would often conduct telephone conversations or check on e-mails, etc. I became an administrative assistant to him, taking dictation, initiating phone calls, and delivering and picking up mail from school. My duties ended when he died, and I missed "the work."

The other surprisingly huge void in my life was the extended family that we had established over the years at the hospital. Even though we were pushed into the setting, many of John's caregivers had become part of our circle of friends that we enjoyed visiting with on a weekly or bi-weekly basis.

I missed seeing them. People cross our paths throughout our lives. Some we stay connected with and others we do not. The staff was now providing other patients and their families with the same level of compassionate care that we had received so there was no time or reason to stay connected with them. It was like another death.

John and I had been shopping for some time for new furniture for our family room. As I had mentioned before, our daughter, Julie, and her family were living with me. She suggested that I continue looking to replace the furniture. John and I had always shopped for the big-ticket items together. This would be the first time that I would be shopping for a big item on my own. Since Julie's baby was only three months old, she suggested that I go look and if I found anything that I liked she would go back with me to the furniture store before I made a final decision. I would have been happy to duplicate what I had by reupholstering the old chair, but the fabric was no longer available. I found something in a local furniture store that I liked, and it was less expensive than reupholstering the old furniture. The new fabric was a very different style and I really wanted a second opinion. The saleswoman was very patient with me and suggested that she would write down what I had selected, and she would loan me fabric samples so that I could see them in the light of my own home. As I was signing the paperwork to borrow the fabric, the Phillip Phillips' song, "Home," played on the store's sound system. This was a song that both John and I liked very much and I can only guess that through this music, it was a sign of approval of my choice.

A few days later, I returned with my daughter to the store so that she could see and actually sit in the floor samples of the couch and chair that I wanted to order. As I sat down to sign the contract for the order, what came on the sound system again but "Home." I said to Julie, "I guess

Dad really likes my choice." I cannot tell you how many times music that John and I both enjoyed has come on at eerily "coincidental" times.

———✠———

November 14, 2013

Dear Family and Friends:

It is hard to believe that tomorrow marks the six-month anniversary of John's death. Many of you have asked how we are doing. Since we cross paths with some more regularly than others I thought I would send out an update.

The kids and I have been doing well, each grieving in our own way, but all healthy expressions of emotion, both happy and sad.

Life will never be the same, but the extreme lows and unanticipated outbursts of grief have become less frequent with time. Bereavement counselors tell you that you have to confront your grief to properly mourn the loss of someone you love. This is really hard work, but otherwise the overwhelming emotions of sadness will remain with you for months, years, or even for the rest of your life. So, we have given in to crying. It does help.

My family and I have been supported by all of you throughout our journey. You have helped to sustain us all through some pretty dark days by spending time with us and by sharing wonderful stories and your personal memories of John. I continue to be blessed by my faith and trust in God that He has put you in our path to help us find peace and contentment.

This spring, John had promised our eight-year-old grandson a new bicycle. We never got around to getting it for him. Three weeks after John died, Zachary rode the three-mile Pan Mass Bike Challenge for Kids to raise money for cancer research. By reaching a certain threshold of donations, he qualified for a raffle. His name was drawn: Zachary had won the top prize of a brand-new bicycle of his choice from a local bicycle shop! Zach said to his mother, "I didn't expect Grandpa to have so much pull so soon!"

This summer, the kids, grandkids, and I went to Stowe, Vermont for our annual visit to the Trapp Family Lodge. It was difficult because we had so many happy memories of John being there. The mountains were breathtaking because the weather was beautiful with the exception of a couple of showers that left the sky streaked with six different rainbows—some of them doubles. Our grandkids all felt John had some part in painting the sky for us. Again, Grandpa can do anything!

The first couple of weeks in September I found particularly difficult, so I worked on some Christmas projects. A friend asked me to join her on a trip to Pittsburgh to visit Falling Waters, a Frank Lloyd Wright designed house that John and I had wanted to visit. It was absolutely beautiful and there were so many wonderful sights to see in Pittsburgh.

John and I were very fortunate to be able to travel as often as we did, especially in the last five years. We were looking forward to a trip to Spain that, in the end, we didn't take. When our high school classmates, the Leonards, asked if I wanted to travel anywhere in Europe that fall, I suggested that we take the trip to Spain that John and I had planned to go on. We visited

Barcelona, Granada, Ronda, Cordoba, Seville, and Madrid. Throughout the trip I thought of how much John would have enjoyed everything we saw and did and again I felt his presence.

Designing the memorial for John's grave has been a daunting task. John and I had selected the lot and the type of stone together, but surprisingly, he had just two requests for what he wanted inscribed on the stone: "No Regrets" and "He is not here, he is in a meeting!" I didn't like either idea, but I did want to respect his wishes. I went to work to write an epitaph that would capture the essence of John and me since I also will be buried in this lot. I finally came up with the following: "In life, love and do good. In death, there are no regrets. In memory, love lives on."

As my family anticipates the holidays, we know that we will be sad at times. But we will also remember how John would want us to look forward to these days with great joy and excitement. He always had high expectations of all of us. It was part of his charm! My hope is that all of you will cherish your memories of John as much as I do by focusing on all the good that surrounds us and by celebrating each day with the people we love as God's gifts to us as we journey through life.

In friendship and love,
Margaret

May 11, 2014

Dear Family and Friends:

This week we will observe the first anniversary of John's death. In some ways, it is hard to believe that we have cycled through all of the seasons: the holidays, the birthdays, and the anniversaries that mark a calendar year. Three hundred and sixty-five days of taking one day at a time. It has been hard work but definitely worth the effort. John would want us to live in the moment and to celebrate each day as a gift and so we have. And I know he is proud of our efforts and success thus far.

Christmas was John's favorite time of year because the season brings the messages of hope and love. He enjoyed decorating the house, he thrived on shopping for that something special and, more recently, he loved sharing the magic of the season with our grandchildren. For all of these reasons, our family was especially anxious about this year's celebration of the holiday. John was surely present as each of us made a conscious effort to appreciate the season and enjoy Christmas Day.

All of it was made easier by our son Christopher's announcement that he and his family would be moving back to the area from Charlotte, NC. Somehow, I had to feel that John had a hand in this. It was the best news we could have received this Christmas. They moved in March and now Chris, Liz, and the boys live just a few miles away. In fact, the day they moved, we spotted a cardinal in a tree outside their home in their new backyard. We think John was so happy to welcome Chris and his family home.

Although we had observed John's birthday in August, I think we were all surprised that the observance of our own birthdays, which start right after Christmas, was very difficult. It wasn't like John traditionally baked a cake, but it was hard to mark the occasion without him being physically present. Again, we shared stories of birthdays we had all shared together and the memories made the days special.

In late January, Julie and Greg realized that they are expecting their second baby. Since Julie had difficulties getting pregnant the first time, this was an extra special blessing. Benjamin, who just turned one in April, will be promoted to big brother to his sister in July. The day Julie got the official news, we again had cardinals in the tree outside our house. We think John was excited by the happy news.

Not to be left out, Heather was informed in April that she has been selected as the new assistant principal of Medfield High School. We all know that John is beaming with pride that she is following in his footsteps.

There have been a myriad of ways that I have tried to reinvent my life without John's physical presence. This spring I took a ten-day trip to Sicily that included three cooking classes. It was a wonderful cultural experience. I can just hear John saying to me, "Oh sure, now you learn how to cook authentic Italian food!"

To offer a tribute to the spirit and legacy John left to Whitman-Hanson, I decided I wanted to create a staff recognition award to the Whitman-Hanson Regional School District. The current superintendent agreed that we would name this the "Dr. John F. McEwan Do What's Best for Kids Award." A review committee will accept nominations and select a staff member or a team who is "doing what is best for kids" by carrying out their duties without expectation of promotion or financial compensation. It will be open to anyone who works for the district. It seemed like the best way to preserve John's belief that every staff member has the potential to make a difference in children's lives.

For those of you who don't live in the area, while John served as the Superintendent of Schools for the Whitman-Hanson Regional School District, he served as the educational leader and visionary who believed that the students of Whitman and Hanson deserved a school that could help them realize their dreams and at the same time, serve as a resource to the residents of both Whitman and Hanson. The school opened in September 2005 and serves as a model school for Massachusetts.

While I was developing the award in John's name, I did not know that there was an effort being made to rename the Whitman Hanson's Performing Arts Center as the "Dr. John F. McEwan Performing Arts Center." Ironically, I got the news in February while I was at Disney World that the school committee approved the idea. There will be a public dedication ceremony on June 10. You know that John would be so humbled to have this tribute made in his honor. He loved to recognize other people's efforts, but never liked to draw attention to himself.

Many of you continue to show your support of our family and me in so many different ways. Each day continues to be a gift. We never know when we wake up in the morning who will impact our day by a seemingly small gesture or kind remark. I can assure you we are grateful for each of you who are put in our path and continue to share your fond memories of John with us.

As my first year of reinvention comes to an end, I reflect on all the people who have touched my life in a special way. I try every day to put my trust in God that I will find the path that He has chosen for me. So far, I have been given very clear direction and I can only pray that this continues. One thing is certain; life does go on. Thank you for being part of mine.

In love and friendship,
Margaret

20

Moving Forward

*The way you get meaning in your life is to
devote yourself to loving others, devote yourself
to the community, and devote yourself to
something that gives you purpose and meaning.*
—Morrie Schwartz, *Tuesdays with Morrie*

We continue to celebrate John's life through the people whose lives he touched and the many happy memories we shared. As we mourn the loss of his physical presence we keep our eyes, ears, and hearts open to signs of his continued presence in our lives. Life is forever changed, but we are so much richer for having shared it with him.

With all that we went through on our journey, I firmly believe that we were given the gift of cancer so that we would not lose sight of how precious our time was, and to make the most of each day, whatever it brought. For our family, the sighting of a cardinal, which also serves as the mascot to John's high school alma mater, lets us know that John is right there with us. It is uncanny how many times one or several cardinals have "shown up" when something special happens.

———〰———

May 13, 2015

Dear Family and Friends:

This week marks the second anniversary of John's death. Some feel that the second year is even more difficult than the first. I am not sure that is true, but I have come to believe that a grieving heart is like a chronic illness. The initial diagnosis of an illness is shocking just like the finality of death. It is hard to imagine how you will cope and how life can go on. There are many days that are a lot better than others but, like a chronic illness, the condition of sadness never leaves you. You look for and find reasons for hope and purpose. Often it comes when a song is played at just the right time, when you see the delight of your grandchildren at play, or a new opportunity presents itself.

During the first year, I think you hope that one day you will wake up and feel healed. Over the course of the second year, you are forced to confront the fact that there is no "cure." There are times that you don't feel so intensely sad but then you "relapse" into a day of grief that makes you realize that you cannot be cured, but you can hope to feel better. You know you have felt better and you will again. Perhaps it is this realization that you have to continue to confront your feelings and emotions that makes the second year harder. I have been told that the feelings of sadness are less intense as the years go on; I am optimistic that this will happen in time.

Over the course of two years, I have learned that coping with death gives us a new appreciation for life and living in the present. As others have experienced similar losses in their lives, the pain of what they now must face makes death hard to accept on a whole new level. It is my hope that my family has been able to provide support to another person or family who must cope with death. It gives purpose to your own sadness and some comfort to someone else.

All of the McEwans have received many blessings as we adjust to living without John physically present in our daily lives. We regularly share stories of how John would react to different situations. Hate is a strong word, but he would have hated the weather this winter. He always said snow should be visited; you should not have to live around it.

Life does go on. There is always transition in a growing family, some imposed and some organic. Over this past year, there have been many changes in my children's lives. Each of them has bought and sold a home. They are blessed to live in homes that reflect their personalities and family's needs. Everyone has shared stories about how John would have approached making a major move. He also would have had a strong opinion about where to place the Christmas tree in each house. No surprise there!

In July, Julie and Greg had a healthy baby girl, Hannah Evelyn. Benjamin became a big brother at 15 months. This is a very busy but happy household. We have been truly blessed with six grandchildren. It is such a joy to watch each of them grow and develop into the person he/she will become. Equally delightful is to observe your own children parent their children. John would be and is so proud of all of them.

Counselors tell us that establishing some kind of legacy in the name of the person helps to perpetuate their memory for the family and others. Last year Whitman-Hanson Regional School District dedicated the Performing Arts Center at the high school to John. It was a beautiful ceremony. Now every time something is going on at the Whitman-Hanson auditorium, it is referred to as the Dr. John F. McEwan Performing Arts Center. John would have been humbled by the tribute but ecstatic over the programs that are now offered in this venue for the two communities. This in itself is a legacy.

Last fall, through the John F. McEwan Memorial Scholarship at Cardinal Spellman, four upper classmen were awarded partial scholarships that allowed them to continue their education at Spellman. This is the same type of scholarship John received when he attended school there. This fall, the first Dr. John F. McEwan "Do What's Best for Kids Award" will be presented at Whitman-Hanson. My family and I established this award to recognize someone who performs above and beyond their job responsibilities to help kids. It seemed a fitting tribute to preserve John's belief that every staff member has the potential to make a difference in children's lives.

As for me, I took a Danube River cruise from Budapest to Prague. John and I had planned to take this trip, but we were forced to cancel. He would have loved the itinerary and there were so many times I felt he was right there with me. Next fall I am planning a trip to Australia and New Zealand.

This is something that I have wanted to do but it was not high on John's list. We shall see how this adventure goes.

This winter allowed me much time to devote to quilting. It has been so therapeutic for me to be able to create something out of bolts of cloth. I also spent time collating the e-mails and letters that John and I wrote over the five years of his illness. It has been a challenging process, but I do feel that it has helped me to grieve and to bring closure to that chapter of my life. Perhaps I will pursue getting this chronicle printed so that others who are living with cancer may find some hope in living fully and to encourage them to cherish every day.

A friend gave me a wonderful book entitled *How to Heal a Grieving Heart*. On the topic of priorities, the authors write: "It is important to know that the amount of love we have left behind for others is all that matters." John knew this in the way he lived his life fully and with joy. So many people benefited from the time he shared with all of us.

John and I enjoyed Kristin Chenoweth. I have a new favorite song she recorded on her *Coming Home* CD entitled, "I Was Here." The lyrics talk about making a difference in the time we are given. My goal each day is to thank God for the blessings I have and to find hope and purpose in my new life because every day is a gift. I do not believe in coincidences, I believe we have all been put on this earth to do God's work and therefore find our purpose in life. We cross paths with people and situations for a reason. My life has changed but I am continuing to find new paths in my journey.

Thank you for continuing to share your stories of John, your memories both happy and sad, because "The best part of life's journey is who you get to share it with." Thank you for being part of mine.

In love and friendship,

Margaret

CHAPTER

21

A New Purpose for This Journey

Every day may not be glorious, but there is something glorious in every day. Find the glory!
—Caleb, *365 Days of Wonder* by R.J. Palacio

In May 2016, I attended a Symposium sponsored by the Melanoma Foundation of New England about the advances in the treatment of melanoma. John's oncologist, Dr. Donald Lawrence, was one of the presenters. It was wonderful to see him and to hear about the continued advances and success in the treatment of melanoma over the past three years.

The most exciting news for me confirmed that FDA had approved MDX-1106, the clinical trial drug that successfully treated John's Stage IV tumors for two and a half years, under the name Opdivo. (Coincidentally, the FDA's announcement of approval was December 22, 2014. This would have been our 42nd wedding anniversary.)

John was eager to use his cancer diagnosis for the benefit of others. We were so fortunate that he was on the cutting edge of melanoma research and that he had the opportunity to benefit from this drug five years before it was put on the market. He would be very happy that the drug now is approved so that others can be treated with a treatment plan that extends their lives with quality time and minimal side effects. These clinical trial drugs continue to deliver hope now and in the future for so many.

—⁓—

May 16, 2016

Dear Family and Friends:

It has been three years since John passed away. I was not planning to send out anything this year, but I decided I needed to write some thoughts down. On and off over the past two years, as many of you had suggested, I have collated the e-mails that I had sent out over the five years of John's cancer journey. Together with some letters he wrote to his staff, I have written a chronicle of our journey of hope and his triumph of living every day with purpose. My goal is to one day publish it for the benefit of other families who are on their own cancer journey. Know that this third-year anniversary message will be the last installment of the "book."

Publishing is a whole new learning curve for me, so I have no idea how long this process may take. But it is a new challenge and the process of writing has helped me cope with my grief. Thank you all for your continued thoughts and prayers. I hope many of you will have an ice cream this week and think fondly of John.

Love,

Margaret

—⁓—

—ᵐ—

Thoughts on the Third Anniversary, May 2016

Three years have now passed since John died. Many days can still go slowly but the years seem to pass quickly. The sadness is not as constant, but I am still surprised at times by overwhelming feelings of emotion with a simple reminder of John and our life together. On the third anniversary of his death, I can say that life is full but not complete without John being physically present. I will always miss him.

This winter was very challenging for our family because my sister's husband was hospitalized in failing health for four and a half months. Don and Kathy had shared a double wedding with John and me and a few years ago all four of us had celebrated our 37th wedding anniversary in Greece. Our families grew up and older together. Uncle Don was a kind and caring man who was like a second father to our children. He passed away just five weeks ago. It is another very sad time for our families. Now that I am observing my sister, her children, and grandchildren grieving their loss, I can see firsthand that my family grieves, as much for the loss of the person we loved, as for the family that now must experience grieving a close family member. Perhaps this can be viewed as making progress in processing our own grief.

There are many firsts during the two years following someone's death. One of the memorable firsts for our children was their first birthday celebration without John. They were surprised how sad they were observing the anniversary of their birthdays without him.

Although three years have passed, this is the first year I have celebrated my "real" birthday without him. In 2008, before the cancer diagnosis, we celebrated my leap year birthday at Walt Disney World. (No surprise there!) We had purchased an annual pass for our visit. The guest relations cast member noticed it was my birthday and gave me a big birthday pin to wear. A short time later, another cast member stopped us on Main Street, wished me a happy birthday and asked if we could be available in the park that afternoon to serve as the grand marshals of the Main Street Parade. What a thrill! John could not control his excitement or joy as we waved to guests on our ceremonial drive down Main Street. What a memorable day!

Later that week, on my actual birthday, John and my daughters had planned a surprise birthday/ retirement party for me. When my company was sold, I had been forced into an early retirement, after 36 years with the same employer. John always felt badly that I never had a formal retirement party. He took advantage of my leap year birthday to combine the celebrations. He invited my family, friends, childhood neighbors, my college roommate, past co-workers, and boss to the party at a nice restaurant. What a joyful celebration of life!

Experience teaches us that when things are going along smoothly, you can expect some challenge to be put in your path. Just a few weeks after my birthday celebration, we knew that John had a very disturbing fatty tumor on his head that no longer appeared benign and started to bleed. Our cancer journey began eight years ago. We had five wonderful years that were a blessing given his original prognosis.

This year my actual birthday fell on a Monday, so my children and grandchildren celebrated it on Sunday. It was a wonderful day. In addition, one of the pleasures of being a leap year baby is that many people from your distant past will remember your birthday and surprise you by phone, card, or e-mail. This year was no exception; I heard from many people that I do not hear from frequently. Nevertheless, I was still surprised by how very sad and lonely I felt because I could not share February 29 with John.

As I reflect on the third anniversary of John being taken from this earth, I know that I will always miss him: his energetic joy of living, his laugh, his desire to experience life to the fullest, and his determination that we can find purpose and satisfaction by living in the present. My adult children and their spouses joined me for dinner on May 15 to continue our celebration of John's life and his continued impact on our daily lives. John was definitely with us and enjoyed the party.

After three years, I have learned that love never dies and there will be new firsts to celebrate and some that we must let go. Time itself does not heal; healing comes from within over time. In grieving, we must choose to make the most of whatever time we are given and to continue to find purpose and fulfillment in our lives. We are all on a journey that will someday come to an end. Every day I wake up hoping that I will appreciate the gift of life that I now have and use it wisely. John would expect nothing less of me.

Thank you for continuing to share your stories and memories of John with my family and me. It is

a source of great joy to know that he continues to
inspire and to bring happy memories to your lives
as well.

    Love,

    Margaret

—⟫⟫—

In the fall and winter of 2016–2017, there was a TV ad for
a cancer drug called Opdivo. At the end of the ad, Bristol
Myers Squibb thanked the patients, doctors, and nurses
who participated in the clinical trials that made the product
possible. I had never seen that done before. Opdivo now has
been approved not only in the treatment of advanced cases
of melanoma but for other types of cancers as well.

On May 15, 2017, the fourth anniversary of John's
death, I submitted my first draft of the memoir of our
cancer journey to the publisher and editor. It has been an
emotionally challenging process to relive those five years
with cancer, but it has given me a chance to spend more
quality time with him. It has helped me to grieve and cope
with his death.

The original e-mails helped John and me to communicate with our family and friends as we lived with cancer.
John had hoped that in his retirement he would spend time
writing, something he loved to do. Including his original,
unedited writing in this memoir has given me an opportunity to fulfill his dream. It gives our young grandchildren
an opportunity to get to know their grandfather better and
to learn some lessons from him. His writing also gives the
reader insights into his passion for life, love, and hope.

My purpose and hope for this memoir will be that it
may help you, the reader, or someone you know, hear a
song, see a face, or be the recipient of a random act of kindness and see all of these signs as reason for hope and to find

purpose in your cancer journey. Publishing this memoir gives John, the teacher, another opportunity to demonstrate how to live life to the fullest and fulfill the dream of giving purpose to why things happen. Together again, in writing this memoir, we have realized a dream! As Morrie Schwartz tells Mitch Albom, the author of *Tuesdays with Morrie,* "Death ends a life, not a relationship."

During the summer of 2017, my daughter asked if I would like to take a ride to visit John's gravesite. We brought four-year-old Benjamin and three-year-old Hannah out to breakfast and then drove to the cemetery. Julie was always very good about explaining to her children what they were about to do and asked if they had any questions. Both of them had visited the cemetery before so they knew where they were going. Once again, the three-year-old felt compelled to remind me that her Grandpa had died and he was buried in the cemetery.

As we drove into the cemetery Ben announced, "Grammy, Santa is buried here." I asked what made him say that and he said, "Because that stone over there has got a sleigh on it." I can only guess that he had seen a spray of flowers etched into a stone. No sooner had the words come out of Ben's mouth than three-year-old Hannah exuberantly shouted out, "But at Christmastime he comes back to life and gives us presents." Julie and I could not stop laughing and I could just hear John giggling too.

Every day I miss John's companionship and the anticipation of the next shared adventure, whether simple or grand. Each day I remember his love, the sound of his infectious laughter and the sight of his joyous smile. I also hear him whispering in my ear, "Now keep making the most of each day and find joy."

When you grieve, you think about how desperately sad you are because the person is gone. I remind myself how much sadder it would have been if our paths had never crossed. If we spend all of our time thinking about the past or worrying about the future, we may miss someone or something that brings new joy into our lives in the present. One of my favorite quotes from Dr. Seuss is: "Don't cry because it is over, smile because it happened."

Three-year-old Hannah got it partially right when she said, "Santa comes alive again at Christmas." The spirit of Santa can come into our life every day of the year if we choose to be hopeful and take the time to value the relationships that we have with the people we love. Every day is a gift.

Acknowledgments

With deepest gratitude to my best friend, life
partner, and co-author, John McEwan, who
inspired all of us to make the most of every day.

It takes a village of caregivers to share a cancer journey. Starting with our family, John and I were blessed to have the love and support of our children: Heather, Christopher, and Julie; their spouses: Frank, Elizabeth (Liz), and Greg; and our grandchildren: Zachary, Keira, Maxwell, Trenton, Benjamin, and now Hannah. Our family was the face of hope throughout our cancer journey and continues to be a source of love, hope, and purpose for me.

When a person receives a cancer diagnosis, extended family and friends often do not know what to say; acknowledgement that you are going through a tough time is all that is needed. John's brothers and sister, my sisters and brother, and their spouses shared our cancer journey, each in their own way. I am grateful to all of them.

Friends can be a special source of comfort. The thoughtfulness of an unexpected call, card, or e-mail brings joy into your life and lets you know that through these people, God has not forgotten you. There are so many who were kind to us, but a few deserve a special mention. Jane and Ed Leonard and Jack and Elena Aherne are two couples that have been especially dear and supportive friends. Other longtime friends since Cardinal Spellman High School days are Jim and Peg Ledwell, Joe and Madlyn McPherson, and Joanne Tribulauskas. John's college friend, Gail Duffy, could always make him smile.

As you live, there are people who come into your life and provide thoughtful contact throughout your journey. Bob Lowe was instrumental in reconnecting many of John's former students and staff to let him know, while he was alive, what he meant to them. What a gift! My cousin Pat Wilk, Elaine White, Julie Caruso, Louise Snyder, Maryann Kowalski, Sue O'Brien, Karen McSweeney, Joe Kennedy, Rick Swanson, Sid Russell, Bob Hodge, and Rich Kelley were among those people who always seemed to send cards or e-mails expressing support at just the right time. Thank you.

John was indebted to those who supported him as he worked at his job while living with cancer, specifically: the Whitman-Hanson School Committee, the Cardinal Spellman Board of Trustees, and his administrative assistants, Michelle Kelley Lindberg, and Aimee Wetzel. John mentions several members of the faculty and staff in his letters, but I want to particularly recognize Ruth Gilbert-Whitner, Barry Cosgrove, and Paul Kelly.

John and I were—and I forever will be—grateful to John's medical providers for the quality of life that we both enjoyed for five years while he lived with stage IV melanoma. In particular, I would like to express my deepest admiration and gratitude to John's exceptionally competent and compassionate medical oncology team at Massachusetts General Hospital led by Dr. Donald P. Lawrence, MD. Over the course of his cancer journey, three extraordinarily caring and competent nurse practitioners on Dr. Lawrence's team worked with John. They were Caroline Kuhlman, MS, RNCS, AOCNP; Krista Rubin, NP; and a special mention of Riley Fadden, NP, who proofread an early edition of this manuscript to ensure the accuracy of the oncology terms. Over the years, there were three very special primary care nurses assigned to John who would share a smile and even laugh during our visits: Allison Concannon RN, BSN; Ellen Hansbury, RN; and Danielle Colby LeBlanc, RN, OCN.

Other members of the Massachusetts General Cancer Center were Christina Cardona, patient service coordinator; Marguerite Parkman, RN, clinical trial coordinator; Mohammedi Ahmed; Sarah Belden, and Ryan Merritt. Ryan has stayed in touch while he pursues his medical career.

After John died, several recipients who had appreciated receiving our e-mails encouraged me to publish them because they felt that they would offer others hope. It is to the following people that I am especially indebted for their support and encouragement: Bette Long, Ann Massey, Heidi Flanagan on behalf of Ed Flanagan, and Mark Scharenbroich.

A special thank you to all who helped guide and support this novice author, including Roselyn Kubek, who volunteered to proofread the very first draft for me; Kathy Teahan, who recommended SDP Publishing Solutions; Lisa Akoury-Ross from SDP Publishing Solutions; Lisa Ann Schleipfer from Eden Rivers Editorial Services who has made suggestions that greatly improved the content, organization, and narrative of our journey; Howard Johnson, who so skillfully created the cover and interior design and layout; and Karen Grennan, who is a master proofreader.

Outside of my family, I am deeply indebted to John's cousin, Judi Owens, and a professional friend of John's and now my dear friend, Gerrie Mahoney. Both friends have helped me to grieve freely and openly while offering continued support and unconditional love.

Mass General's Social Service Department extended an invitation to join a bereavement group that was led by the very capable and understanding Todd Rinehart, LICSW, ACHP-SW. To that special group, thank you for your support and unique understanding: Evie, Anne, Marsha, Carole, Kathy, Janice, and Jack.

To Michele Stenson and my fellow quilters that have helped me to reinvent myself through a renewed passion for creative sewing and quilting at Michele's shop, American Folk Art and Craft Supply. And to my colleagues who work and volunteer with me at My Brother's Keeper and keep me grounded in how to serve others by delivering love and hope to people in need.

And last, but not least, IMPACT Melanoma that provides ongoing education, prevention, and support for skin cancer. And the Massachusetts General Hospital Cancer Center and the MGH Melanoma Research Foundation that continue to conduct research into new and improved treatments that deliver hope for so many.

About the Authors

Although their early years were spent in the same town, John and Margaret did not know each other until high school. Married for over 40 years, the McEwans loved to spend time with their three married children and their now six grandchildren. The couple traveled as often as they could internationally and would go on annual family vacations, especially to Walt Disney World and the Trapp Family Lodge in Stowe, Vermont.

John began his advanced education in the seminary but then redirected his goal of serving people through a career in education. He began as an English teacher and moved into administrative positions: principal, superintendent of schools, and first lay president of his high school alma mater. John received several awards over the course of his career: the 2000 Massachusetts Principal of the Year, the 2009 Massachusetts School Counselor Association Administrator of the Year, and was named to the Jostens Renaissance Hall of Fame.

Margaret holds a bachelor's of science and master's degree in food and nutrition. As a registered dietitian, she was a trailblazer in the field of supermarket retail dietetics, and was the first female vice president of Shaw's Supermarkets. She retired as Shaw's Vice President of Corporate Communications in 2004.

Margaret enjoys spending time with her family and volunteering for My Brother's Keeper, a Christian ministry that provides hope and love to families in need. Much of her creative free time is spent quilting and embroidering household items and decorative art for her family and friends. This book is her first published work, but she has enjoyed the experience and may consider doing more creative writing in the future.

Every Day Is a Gift
A Couple's Cancer Journey
Margaret P. and John F. McEwan

Author website: www.CardinalGifts.net

E-mail: margaret@cardinalgifts.net

Publisher: SDP Publishing

Also available in ebook format

Available at all major bookstores

 **SDP Publishing**

www.SDPPublishing.com

Contact us at: info@SDPPublishing.com

CPSIA information can be obtained
at www.ICGtesting.com
Printed in the USA
BVHW04s1013190518
516751BV00001B/70/P